# CATHOLIC MORAL TEACHING

## IN ITS RELATIONS TO

## MEDICINE AND HYGIENE

By Dr. GEORGE SURBLED

FREELY TRANSLATED FROM THE FRENCH

By THE REV. HUBERT J. EGGEMANN

THE HUMAN ORGANISM IN
HEALTH, DISEASE, AND DEATH

B. HERDER BOOK CO.,
15 & 17 SOUTH BROADWAY, ST. LOUIS, MO.,
AND
33 QUEEN SQUARE, LONDON, W. C.
1930

NIHIL OBSTAT

Sti. Ludovici, die 28. Martii, 1930,

F. J. Holweck,

Censor Librorum

IMPRIMATUR

Sti. Ludovici, die 29. Martii, 1930,

✠ Joannes J. Glennon,

Archiepiscopus

*Vail-Ballou Press, Inc., Binghamton and New York*

# AUTHOR'S PREFACE

*Morality* is the law of human life and honor, and the guarantee of civilization. Religion is based upon it and all the schools of philosophy recognize it. The materialists alone, having decided to lead us back to the state of nature and of barbarism, seek to destroy its foundations; but the necessity of a rule of conduct is so evident that even they do not dare openly to contest it. Posing as the defenders of modern science, they are forced to bring the ancient and immutable laws of morality into conflict with their much vaunted science and to content themselves in laying claim to *scientific morality*.

But there is nothing excessive in this pretension and it agrees very well with the demands of experience and logic; it is also our morality. Morality, far from being a stranger to, finds its necessary foundations in science. By a thousand points of contact it is connected with physiology, hygiene, medicine, and all the sciences that are concerned with our physical nature. Is there anything surprising in this? Is it not rather the necessary result of that intimate union of body and soul which constitutes man? Would it be possible to know the human soul without the organism which serves as its *substratum* and instrument?

To study the relation of the moral to the natural laws, to compare and reconcile the teachings of science with those of reason, the conclusions of philosophy with those of theology, is the purpose of this work and the high aim we hope to accomplish.

The task is immense, almost alarming, but it is urgently necessary, and that is our excuse for having undertaken it. Works on moral theology, as well as on pure science, abound; but treatises which unite the two and seek to bring the teaching of the Church into harmonious agreement with the results of experience, are rare and insufficient. The writers favored by former generations are antiquated, incomplete, and of doubtful utility. Let us be frank and say that, at the present day, there is no serious and commendable work on the grave problems which daily present themselves for the scrutiny of the moralist and the physician. May our modest production help to fill this deplorable lacuna!

The relations of moral teaching to medicine and hygiene are many and incessant; we have, in this work, not attempted to deal with all of them, but only with those most important from the viewpoint of practical life. In the first part we shall study *Organic Life*. The second will be devoted to the study of *Psycho-Cerebral Life,* and all ques-

tions pertaining to this subject will be, if not eluci-
dated, at least broached and examined. The third
part will be dedicated to a study of the *Sexual Life*.[1]

Learned theologians have been good enough to
revise and correct our manuscript; and we wish
hereby to express to them our lively gratitude. Their
encouragement is, after God, our greatest safeguard.

An humble soldier in the grandest and most beautiful cause, we have devoted our mind, our will and
all our ardor to this cause, but we intend to be second to none in respect and obedience. A faithful
child of Holy Mother Church we accept without
reservation all the orders of ecclesiastical authority
and submit in advance to all its decisions in regard
to everything, that may be judged temerarious or
erroneous in the following lines.

TRANSLATORS' NOTE.—We have followed the arrangement of
Dr. Albert Sleumer's German version. Dr. Surbled devoted his
first two volumes to the study of sexual life; we make his
Volume III our Volume I, and his Volume IV our Volume II.

# AUTHOR'S PREFACE TO THE SECOND EDITION

The first edition of this work was sold in a few months. This unexpected success has imposed upon us the duty of revising and developing our work and of rendering it more worthy of the honest and enlightened public to which it is addressed. We do not hide from ourselves the imperfections of our work; but the precious encouragements that we have received, and which do not cease to pour in upon us, make us hope that we are doing some good.[1]

Furthermore, this is not the time for reserve, silence or solitary sighs on the audacity of materialism and the progress of immorality; it is the time to labor, to combat error publicly, and to give an account of the faith that is in us.

Our adversaries are flooding the world with unhealthy, false, and dangerous books which corrupt and ruin thousands of souls. We must oppose them at every point, fearlessly and incessantly, with

[1] At least a dozen high ecclesiastical dignitaries wrote letters of encouragement and commendation to Dr. Surbled, among them Cardinal Bourret, Archbishop of Rodez.

the luminous and victorious teachings of truth.

True, in the plans of Divine Providence we are but *"useless servants,"* but we will never be, so please God, lax or lazy. We will daily fight the good fight, always remembering the maxim and the glorious example of that valiant apostle and noble martyr, Père Captier: "Forward for the cause of God!"

TRANSLATORS' NOTE.—After the eloquent preface of the scholarly French author, there is no need of any special preface to this authorized English edition of his learned and useful work. We only wish to remark that, in presenting this volume to the English-speaking public, we have retained the medical terminology of the original only, when not wholly obsolete. A few references to English and German works, and a few footnotes not contained in the original, have been added. The translator is indebted to Joseph Grindon, M.D., and Mr. Arthur Preuss, Editor of the *Fortnightly Review,* for valuable assistance in the editing of his manuscript and the correction of the proofsheets.

If this volume meets with public favor, it is proposed to issue the others of the same series in an English adaptation.

H. J. E.

# CONTENTS

## PART I
## THE HEART

## PART II
## THE NUTRITIVE LIFE

# CONTENTS
## PART III
## DISEASE

## PART IV
## DEATH

# PART I
# THE HEART

# CHAPTER I

## HEART AND BRAIN

THE central and motor organ of blood circulation is the *heart;* but it is so intimately connected with sense life, and records and transmits the individual movements of the latter so instantaneously and so accurately that it was long mistaken for the *brain,* the real organ of sense perception. Numerous activities of the nerve centers were incorrectly ascribed to the heart, though its movements were obviously only the necessary effect of such activities.

We must not forget, however, that physiology is a modern science, that our positive knowledge of the nervous system is very recent, and that, in consequence of the widespread ignorance of the functions of various organisms, and especially of the brain, the ancients long considered the heart as the center of soul life, as the source of sense perception, as the organ of the affections, and as the seat of the passions. In this regard scholars and philosophers agreed with the poets, and the latter gave expression to the general opinion.

The heart, as the supposed principle of nerve force, seemed to occupy the first place in man and to regulate all his vital activities. Harvey's [1] great discovery could not eradicate this grave error and Descartes' [2] hypothesis of *animal spirits* merely confirmed instead of destroying it. Whence, in the opinion of this celebrated revolutionary, do these *animal spirits,* which we to-day designate as *nerve currents,* really originate? They do not originate (according to Descartes) in the nerves nor in the brain, but are produced by the heart itself and by its movements. There the blood is beaten and heated, its liveliest and most subtle particles ("spirits" or "vapors") mount to the brain, which they excite and move and thence finally enter into the various nerves of the bodily structure. These nerves are hollow tubes filled with marrow, similar to the substance of the brain; thither the "spirits" flow and thus enter into the circulation.[3]

Need we remark that such theories are the ingenious products of a vivid imagination and of gratuitous hypotheses which modern physiology cannot accept? The central nervous system sends out many

[1] William Harvey (1578–1657) was physician in ordinary to James I and Charles I of England. His best known work is, *De Circulatione Sanguinis,* Rotterdam, 1649.

[2] Réné Descartes (1596–1650) wished to transform philosophy according to the pattern of the "only rational" science, *i. e.,* mathematics. As the fundamental basis of his philosophy he placed the certainty of existence (*cogito, ergo sum*).

[3] See Descartes' *Traité de l'Homme; les Passions,* and Bossuet, *Connaissance de Dieu et de soi-même.*

fibers to the heart, but receives no other fluid from it than blood. The nerves are by no means hollow tubes. The nerve impulses do not originate in, but are independent of, the heart. In a word, the *animal spirits* so popular in the seventeenth century no longer exist, but have justly become discredited. Yet in this matter we shall be very careful not to slander the physiology of that great century; on the contrary, we humbly confess that the *nerve impulses* which have been substituted for the *animal vapors* of the Cartesians, have only served to substitute new problems for old ones.

Research has established the fact that the heart is an organ marvellously well supplied with nerves. Its muscular substance is permeated in every direction by a network of nerve fibers, which by means of the microscope can be followed into the elementary muscle fibers, and which, moreover, are accompanied by nerve ganglia and nerve cells. This incomparable abundance of nerves in the heart, which, with every lively emotion elicits a more or less noticeable echo in the heart-beats, and which to some extent permits this organ of circulation to participate in psychic life, explains, without, of course, justifying, the error of the ancients. Such a hypothesis is as dangerous as it is false, and we must refute it the more decidedly since, based upon popular instinct, it still leads numerous minds astray.

The widespread opinion which makes the heart the center of the affections and a symbol of love, need not disturb us, as it is not based upon strict observation, but founded upon a vague presumption. It merely gives expression to the echo which the agitations of sensibility elicit in the organ of circulation, and substitutes the effect for the cause.

In this respect sense illusions are very numerous; yet they do not lead reason astray. For example, no one doubts the movement of the earth, and yet everyone speaks of the sun as rising and setting, because our eyes know only the appearances. To quote another example, hygienists know very well that a choleric (from χολή, gall) temperament has no relation whatever to the condition of the liver, but depends upon the central nervous system, and yet the common phrase remains in use, because it gives expression to one of the clearest manifestations of the irritable temperament. Thus, too, we hold as certain that the brain is the seat of the passions and of sensibility, yet we retain the custom of designating the emotions as affections or sentiments of the heart, because these emotions, emanating from the brain, inevitably and often but too perceptibly affect the heart.

That the brain is in reality the organ of sensibility, has been irrefutably established by numerous laboratory experiments. An animal whose entire brain has been removed, becomes *insensible* to its surroundings, and to the loudest noises; it falls into a deep sleep, a sort of coma. It may be wounded, pieces of tissue, even a member, may be torn from its body, and yet it seems not to be *affected*. Unconscious reflex movements are the only response to these violent excitations; and, if it be permitted to say that the mutilated animal still *feels* pain, we are at any rate obliged to admit that its sensibility has been greatly diminished, nay, well nigh extinguished. Nevertheless, the heart still functions as the organ of circulation; its always normal pulsations force the blood into the arteries and maintain the life of the various organs. Hence we must assert that the removal of the nerve centers suppresses sensibility, while leaving the heart intact.

The proof *ex opposito* is decisive. It is certainly impossible to suppress the heart and larger blood vessels in the higher vertebrates; yet it is comparatively easy to remove them in the case of frogs. In this latter case we notice that sensibility remains intact. From this it follows that the latter stands in no causal relation to the central organ of blood circulation.

Clinical observations furthermore reveal that diseases of the heart exert no immediate influence upon the sensible affections. Though an individual be suffering from some serious lesion of the valves of the heart, the force of his sensibility by no means depends upon the strength of his *fleshly heart,* in fact has nothing to do with it, and his *moral heart* frequently remains firm and courageous, as long as the brain is not affected. On the contrary, sensibility manifests a direct dependence upon cerebral troubles. Without speaking here of the moral confusion which proceeds from insanity, idiocy, hysteria, and all acute or chronic encephalic diseases, we shall cite only the strange, transient mutations of character and sentiment observed at times in pregnant women, as well as in some young mothers (puerperal delirium). These are all of a neurotic character.

From all these facts, which could easily be multiplied, it follows that the brain is the sole organ of sensibility and the true seat of the affections.[4] Nevertheless the heart is bound to the nervous organ by thousands of fibers, and its disturbances, agitations, and perturbations are definite indices of the emotions of the soul. For this reason it is and remains the living symbol of love, which alone betrays the attractions or repulses of that wonderful and sovereign power which decides the fate of men, and which man, by reason of his free will, can deliver to the seductions of evil, to the sway of vice, or which he can direct on the way of goodness, ever higher and higher, beyond the vain appearances of this world, onward to the Supreme Good, the God of love and mercy.

[4] This doctrine, which we uphold, finds abundant proof in embryology and natural history.

# CHAPTER II

THE passions are to the heart, what thoughts are to the soul, and they are of such great importance and so closely interwoven with our life that we could understand neither soul nor body without them. They are sensible movements dependent upon the nerve centers, which emanate in a natural manner from the general perceptive faculty and assure the reciprocal life which they adorn. The physiological knowledge which we possess of these necessary elements of our activity, unfortunately does not go beyond what has just been said.

Where is the exact seat of the passions? Is it in the brain? We are not in possession of accurate data concerning the play, or, as it is incorrectly termed, the "mechanism" of all the passions in general nor of each passion in particular. Science is silent on these points, but the future is full of promise.

The passions are the highest of the animal functions. Their complicated nature will not be clearly understood until the day when physiology will accurately determine the functions of sensibility on which they are grafted. In this regard much work remains to be done. Consciousness, the "common or central sense" (*sensorium commune* of the ancients) must be more accurately located and analyzed as to its nervous elements and functions. The various forms of imagination and memory are as yet practically unexplored. Special sensibility alone is beginning to reveal its secrets. Nerve life, hardly recognized in its first outlines, cannot as yet be explained in detail. But if external observation bristles with difficulties, internal observation is possible and easy; to it, then, we must have recourse.

The passions, which are intimately bound to the organs of sensation, show direct relations with the intellect and will and have a decisive influence on the moral life. Of all modern thinkers Pascal [1] is perhaps the one who has most clearly perceived the rôle of the passions. "It is not sufficient to think," he says, "we must also act." Now, we are urged to act by the passions, which agitate the heart, arouse the senses, and stimulate the will. Between the external world and the soul, between matter and the spirit, the passions, belonging to both, form a logical and necessary link. Strictly speaking, the will is the grand motive power of life and the passions are its main-spring; the one directs, the others execute.

[1] Blaise Pascal (1623–1662), a very talented author. He fell under the influence of the Jansenists and under the pseudonym Louise de Montalte wrote lampoons upon the Jesuits.

The intellect comprehends the truth, the will embraces it, and the passions, obeying the higher faculties, excite the emotions, attach man more and more to the object of his love, and place all their ardor at the disposal of the soul.

The passions, then, participate in the life of the soul, nay, they form part of the soul itself. They are, beyond a doubt, organic animal functions; but the soul, as the mistress of vital operations, exalts and in a manner spiritualizes them. When properly controlled and functioning normally, they admirably serve the intellect and establish such an intimate and indissoluble union between body and soul that our being appears as one. In this sense we may say with Pascal, when speaking of *man*, "the passions are occasioned by the body, but they belong to the spirit, nay, they are the spirit itself."

The passions, which maintain an active intercourse between body and soul, originate either in interior sensations or in sensible impressions, agreeable or disagreeable.

*Pleasure* originates in an agreeable sensation; it is instantaneous and always vivid, whether this sensation be perceived at the moment, or the recollection thereof present itself to the memory. By contrary effect, *pain* repels us and deters us from the experienced or imaginary object. Pleasure as well as pain of every sort elicit in our souls appetites or repugnances which are absolutely instinctive; and it is on these transient sentiments that the more intense and durable movements of sensibility, which constitute the passions, are based.

What, then, is passion, considered in its relation to the soul? Bossuet very accurately defines it as "a movement of the soul which is affected by pleasure or pain, both of which originate in a real or imaginary object, and either pursues the respective object or flees from it." [2]

All philosophy, since the time of Aristotle and the Scholastics, has recognized eleven passions in the human heart. It will suffice to enumerate them here.

*Love* occupies the first place. It is the most elevated form of desire. He who loves seeks to unite himself with an object and endeavors to possess it.

*Hatred,* on the contrary, has for its sole aim to withdraw from an object and to remove it.

*Desire* is the striving for a beloved object that is absent.

*Aversion* is the repugnance felt towards the object of hatred.

*Joy* is the satisfaction experienced by the heart when it possesses and enjoys what it loves and desires.

*Sorrow* is the state of the soul when tormented by an evil from which it cannot escape.

[2] Bossuet, *op. cit.,* (see note 3), c. i. § 6.

These six constitute the so-called *concupiscible passions*. For them to come into existence or increase, the presence or absence of their respective objects is all that is required. The five other passions, called *irascible*, are differentiated from the former by the difficulties to be vanquished or the effort to be made.

*Audacity* (boldness or courage) persists in uniting itself to a beloved object in spite of obstacles.

*Fear* endeavors to withdraw us from some well nigh inevitable evil.

*Hope* appears only in respect to the acquisition of some good, which is the more sought after, the less its acquisition is assured.

*Despair* is evoked by the true or false conviction that the hoped-for good can never be attained.

*Anger* strives to free us by violence from that which causes us pain, or to take revenge on such an object.

Besides these eleven passions the following are also enumerated: *dread, fright, horror, terror, anxiety, envy, emulation, admiration, astonishment,* etc. But these emotions deserve no special classification since they can easily be reduced to the aforementioned passions, as we shall show later.

Uneasiness and anxiety are of the same nature as fear; dread, fright, horror, and terror are but exaggerated forms of fear.

Admiration is a complex emotion, which comprises love, joy, and desire all at once; love of a beautiful object, joy at contemplating it, and the desire to analyze its effects.

Astonishment approaches uneasiness and fear.

Emulation contains both hope and audacity: the hope of being able to perform the good actions which others have undertaken, and the audacity to carry them on with confidence of success.

Shame participates in the nature of sorrow and of fear: sorrow at having committed some fault, and fear of bringing upon oneself contempt or hatred.

Envy, in its various degrees, is characterized by sorrow, which we experience at the sight of another's prosperity, by fear of being deprived of such a good, by despair of acquiring this good, and by hatred of its possessor.

Thus we find the ancient nomenclature of the passions confirmed. But not all psychologists content themselves with this simple recital. A number maintain, and not without reason, that these eleven passions are further reducible. Thus anger, aversion, and hatred have the same origin and the same tendency. Sorrow, too, and despair are very closely related. Hope and desire seem to be but two sides of the same passion.

This interrelation of the passions is very evident and has struck all thinkers. They all reveal a certain relationship, but they by no means permit of complete assimilation. As has been well said, the passions are sisters and have a common bond, *i. e.,* *love*. Love is the origin of all the movements of our sensibility, the first of the passions, and the source of all the others. "Take away love," says Bossuet, "and no passion remains; feed love, and you will cause all passions to grow." [3]

[3] *Ibid,* c. i. § 6.

# CHAPTER III

PASSION is the highest form of sensibility, the chief element of our action, the docile and necessary hand-maid of the will, and a precious instrument of intellectual and moral progress.

Such is the doctrine handed down by traditional philosophy and which seems to us to afford the most exact notion of the passions. But when we leave the domain of the absolute or, to be more precise, of pure and exalted spirits, in order to consider the great mass of humanity and ordinary life with its dangers and temptations, we are constrained to admit that our viewpoint changes and that, in practice, the passions but too frequently fail to perform the beautiful task assigned to them by nature. When the intellect errs or the will weakens, passion places itself at the service of error and vice, and the hierarchy of the powers of our soul is upset. Unfortunately, such accidents are by no means rare. The life of mankind, nay, the life of every one of us, is replete with such instances; but the responsibility must not necessarily be charged to blind animal passion, but rather to a poorly enlightened intellect or a culpable will. If education has not developed the will, if the character is incapable of restraining the lower tendencies and desires of nature, or does not vanquish them whenever they stir, the "heart" usurps control, and draws man, whom it entirely dominates, into disorder and grievous excesses. Is not this the history of the life—and death of many a soul?

The cruel and painful division of our being between the violent movements of the heart and the cold voice of reason, this perpetual and too often unequal struggle between the spirit and the body, constitutes a great and fearful mystery which has been recognized and studied by the philosophers of all times, but which philosophy alone can never penetrate. The key to this mystery is not accessible to human reason, but it is furnished by faith. Our incessant struggle, our vacillation between pleasure and duty, our weaknesses, errors, and faults, result from original sin. To this man must ascribe the fact that his reason is so frequently blind, that his life is so restless, that he is incapable of recognizing the truth or of finding his way by his own power on the path of virtue. Sin has plunged him into misery and death; his spirit is obscured, his will is weakened at the very moment when the body, which really should have obeyed, rebels, assumes control, and but too often becomes the tyrant of the dethroned soul. As St. Augustine admirably writes, "Man, this scion of the Spirit, should be spiritual even in his flesh, yet he is become carnal even in his soul." [1]

Yea, that is "the old Adam," *the carnally-minded man,* the "human beast" shaped by original sin, so well described by the teachers of the faith, as we unfortunately rediscover him in ourselves. This *flesh*—let us not forget it—is at the same time body and soul; but the soul is always the source of evil. "It is not the corruptible flesh," says St. Augustine, "which makes the soul sinful; on the contrary, it is the sinful soul which has made the flesh corruptible." [2]

Fortunately God showed mercy to fallen humanity and our birth from Adam's seed has been compensated in an ineffable manner by our rebirth in Jesus Christ. Nevertheless the flesh and the spirit remain in an incessant struggle; and in order to respond to grace, the soul must conquer its passions and subject them to the control of the will.

The passions are an integral part of our nature, but their disorders are so frequent, so productive of pain and disaster, that we easily overlook their good qualities and frequently know them only in their excesses. These deplorable excesses generally are called

[1] *De Civitate Dei,* l. XIV, c. 15.
[2] *Ibid.,* c. 3.

by the name of "passions"—an abuse of language which is *per se* of no particular consequence, but becomes intolerable when we meet it in the works of certain philosophers, because it contradicts both truth and logic. The passions, we are told, are movements of the sensibility, which take possession of the attention, confuse the judgment, paralyze liberty, and inevitably lead us into excesses, in which we sacrifice our reason, our interests, and our duty. M. Franck, above all, is quite categorical in confusing these disorders of the passions with the passions themselves. "The passions," he writes, "far from being, as is constantly repeated, the faithful expression of the laws of nature, are precisely the contrary and must not be considered less dangerous in the physical than in the moral order. The laws of nature and the instincts, the primitive impulses by which they make themselves known to sensible beings, have a perfectly determined purpose, an exact limit, and an invariable end; such are, for example, the appetites which direct the life of animals. The passions, no less foreign to the animal than the desires,[3] admit of neither end nor truce nor obstacle; they carry us away in their

[3] This is a grave error, evidently inspired by Cartesian automatism. But it cannot stand in the light of observation. An animal has impulses, desires, and passions just as we have, but it has neither the intelligence nor the will, nor even the fertile imagination, of man, which give so large an extension and such formidable strength to the movements of the heart.

impetuous movements until they crush us. Like fire, by which they have been frequently represented, they do not abandon their prey until they have consumed it." [4]

These are briefly the deplorable effects of the passions, *when unrestrained*. We know them; but we also know the useful rôle played by these impulses of our sensible nature and the utter impossibility of stifling them in their source. On principle we may not condemn the passions; for if they fill their normal place under the direction of reason, they constitute human life itself and contribute to its perfection. We can no more suppress these necessary movements of sensibility than we can suppress the beating of the heart or the respiratory activity of the lungs. They constitute an integral part of our organism, but, like all other elements of life, are subject to alteration. Passionate excesses are no more the passions than sophisms are judgments; they are errors and faults, which a wise control should prevent and which an energetic will can rectify.

The passions were made to serve reason, not to enslave it; and if this truth is all too frequently forgotten, this does not change the nature of things, which it has seemed useful for us to establish before approaching the painful study of the disorders of sensibility.

[4] Art. "Passions" in *Dict. des Sciences Philos.*, 2nd ed., p. 1264.

Excesses of passion occur with dreadful frequency. They are the source of our ills. Hygiene as well as ethics severely condemn them. They imperil and frequently ruin not only the soul, but also the body. A rapid sketch of their pernicious effects seems appropriate here.

Courage is a noble passion, but it must be ruled by reason. Besides courageous men, there are the foolhardy who undertake actions whose purpose, importance, and dangers they have not calculated. Reason does not guide them. They blindly obey instinctive forces, the inspiration of the moment, the promptings of folly and pride. In a thousand ways they imperil their health and their lives; the accidents, however, that they meet with are but the well-deserved recompense of their imprudence.

If hope is the daughter of Heaven and "giveth life," desire, when left to itself, soon exceeds the limits of reason, and grows, increases, and exalts itself unduly. *Vires acquirit eundo.* Its constancy and growing ardor produce a dangerous concentration of nervous activity which dries up the heart and quickly exhausts the strength.

In all our actions, desire, when not governed by reason, exposes us to errors and imprudences. Even in the love of God it may prove perilous to holy souls, because at times it may cause them to forget and neglect everything else, even to the detriment of faith. Here, on the authority of Bishop Bougaud,[5] we cite a charming trait of monastic heroism. "When the saintly Père Muard presented a rule of dreadful austerity at Rome, Pius IX smiled and said, 'Now, now, what are you doing with that little beast?' And with his pontifical hand he struck out the impossible prescriptions." Even though the aspirations of a pious soul are infinite, nature is weak and limited, and the authority of the Church knows how to harmonize its demands with reason. But we will not insist on this vast and luminous aspect of the question, which to some extent withdraws itself from our competence and which we shall find again later; rather let us study the terrestrial aspect of the question, where the sins of excess are much more grievous and frequent.

The less a man is attached to eternal things, the more is he tormented by the inordinate desire for perishable goods. This desire causes deceptions and misery. By raising the cost of living, by developing beyond measure the taste for luxury and good living, by causing an implacable struggle for life, the conditions of modern society have created new and factitious needs and insatiable desires. The ambition for honors and the love of riches have taken possession of the hearts of men, are agitating and ruining

[5] Emil Bougaud, Bishop of Laval, *Le Christianisme et les Temps Présents,* t. IV, p. 537.

them. The life of even the humblest is troubled. For the few fortunate ones who attain their goal, how many unfortunates succumb! Against one favorable chance, how many contrary chances! What bitter disillusionments! What disastrous falls!

The cerebral exaltation provoked by this insensate course of the world toward happiness, has a deplorable result which is recorded by statistics. It fills the asylums with insane and the cemeteries with suicides.

Material pleasures tempt us; the lowest make the strongest appeal to the heart. Without speaking here of the guilty desires of lust and avarice we note those which induce men to excesses in eating and drinking and which are as frequent as they are difficult to master. The dangers to which they expose men are well known. Gluttony and drunkenness constitute a social plague as well as a capital sin. Merely to state their fearful effects on the body would involve an exposition of the whole of pathology. Medical science makes every effort to bind up the wounds inflicted by intemperance, but unfortunately can effect no cure; hygiene supports moral teaching in upholding the Ten Commandments by insisting that man's sufferings are the consequences of his sins.

Envy, that black passion which grieves and grows furious at the good fortune of others, endangers the health if it is not subdued. It impairs the power of the brain to such an extent that it disturbs the activity of the organs and hinders the process of nutrition. It frequently induces anorexia and emaciation. A proverbial saying concerning the envious is, that "envy dries them up." In some cases the judgment is warped and the use of reason is lost. Childhood is especially exposed to the excesses of envy. Little children have been observed to pine away under the influence of jealousy, with no noticeable trace of any material cause.

A sudden, unexpected, and intense joy produces contradictory and surprising effects. It sometimes causes distress and attacks the heart or brain. It has caused almost instantaneous death by syncope.[6] Leo X died of joy. Hallé narrates the case of a man who suffered an attack of violent delirium and serious fever because he was unexpectedly exonerated by a revolutionary tribunal and recovered only after twenty days. On the other hand joy frequently exercises a beneficent influence upon the condition of the sick and the wounded. A cheering visit, a few assuring and encouraging words, or good news sometimes suffice to restore strength and health.

Fear, together with its allied psychical states, such as dread, fright, uneasiness, worry, is a depressing

[6] Numerous cases of the death of mothers or wives of soldiers, who unexpectedly saw their dear ones return from captivity, when they had been reported dead, are recorded in the history of the World War.

passion, which weakens character and quickly attacks health. Wounded soldiers who are discouraged and pursued by terror are the despair of physicians; delirium and a thousand other accidents lie in wait to conduct them to a speedy, almost certain death. Even therapeutics is powerless in regard to those who are the prey of the foolish suggestions of fear. Great fear manifests itself no less terribly in the case of the healthy. If it is vivid, it shatters the strength and upsets the system. Experience proves that it may cause syncope, and even insanity. The horrible accidents so common in our day often attack the reason of those who have lost neither life nor limb. Fright has an especially terrible effect upon weak, delicate, and nervous constitutions, and above all upon children. It may cause convulsions, nervous disorders, hysteria, etc.

Sorrow, like fear, exercises a debilitating influence on the organism and exposes it to grave perils. Shame, which originates in sorrow, is wholesome and valuable within proper limits, yet everyone well knows that it may cause scrupulosity and its deplorable consequences. Violent grief, which concentrates in the heart and does not find the necessary means of diversion in the consolations of religion, may lead to the grave or to that premature death which is called insanity.

Sorrow gone to excess becomes despair. We need

not here depict the gravity of this gloomy passion or the severe condemnation which it merits. Its physiological effects are the same as those of sorrow and fear. Christian souls either do not know it at all, or, at any rate, have a sure remedy for it. In the case of others it causes the gravest disorders, loss of reason and, as a logical result, suicide.

Of all the passions anger surely is the most common and the most pernicious. In its paroxysms cerebral excitation becomes intense and to some extent paralyzes common sense and free will. As in the actions of the mentally deranged, inhibition of the reasoning faculty permits the acts of the violently angry and almost entirely destroys responsibility. Yet anger is never instantaneous; we feel it approach, we foresee its consequences, we can overcome its attacks, and above all we can flee the occasions thereof.

Violent and especially habitual anger, which no moral or dogmatic precept can prevent or dissipate, exercises a disastrous influence upon the organism. It has been noted that attacks of hysteria, convulsions, nay even death may ensue (Richeraud). Vomiting, jaundice, hemorrhages and skin eruptions are as frequent as nervous troubles. Under the influence of anger wet-nurses suffer loss of milk or notice a change in it. The anger of pregnant women seems to exert a sinister influence upon their unborn children.

Never is anger more terrible than when it is premeditated and voluntary, and when it is nourished by hatred. When these two passions unite, they dominate the person whom faith no longer protects, and are the cause of quarrels and strifes that fill the world and strew it with ruins.

To recapitulate, the unrestrained passions indicate degeneracy of spirit and entail the gravest consequences for the individual as well as for society. They produce only an ephemeral success and frequently meet with their punishment in their own excess. We know the abyss into which they plunge the moral sense; we have seen the physical evils which attend them. Reason, outraged in its rights, seems finally to abandon the guilty man to his victorious passions.

# CHAPTER IV

## CONTROL OF THE PASSIONS

THOSE philosophers and moralists who indiscriminately condemn the passions as a pestilential evil, entirely misapprehended their rôle and purpose. We have demonstrated this mistake in the foregoing chapter. Constrained by evidence, they cannot place all the passions on the same level, but must admit that some are vile, while others are noble; but they believe that each and every passion must be banished from the heart in order that the will may preserve its freedom and the intellect its buoyancy. Their whole moral hygiene is epitomized in the maxim, *"Suppress the passions."*

What reply can be made to this? Do not the passions belong to our nature? Are they not inherent in the cerebral function? Are we free to submit to or to evade their hot embrace? No man can believe this. For where is the heart absolutely insensible to every interest and impregnable to every desire? What human being is devoid of passion?

Passion dwells in the heart of every man, or rather, the heart itself places passion at the service of the will. It is necessary for action, and it develops in proportion as it depends upon a stronger vital energy and a higher intellectual force. The greatest geniuses, as history testifies, have been fostered by an ardent though restrained sensibility, and never was passion more subdued and yet stronger than in the glowing hearts of the Apostles and Saints. This sentiment is admirably expressed by Pascal: "The greater the genius, the stronger the passions. . . . In a great soul everything is great." [1]

In themselves, the passions are neither evil nor destructive; following the inclination of the will, they render either good or detestable service. They always participate in the life of the soul, but they must be subjected to the intellect and directed in the path of virtue. It is here that the important rôle of education is made manifest, and that we can understand the decisive influence which a good training in childhood exercises upon the whole of a man's existence. As Descartes says in his beautiful treatise on the Passions, "It is evident that even those who have the weakest souls can acquire a perfect mastery over all their passions, if sufficient pains are taken to teach and guide them." [2]

The sensations of childhood are vivid and tumultuous; the appetites are unrestrained and boundless;

[1] Pascal, *Discours sur les Passions de l'Amour.*
[2] Pascal, *Des Passions de l'Âme,* art. 50.

the budding reason has neither the power nor sufficient discernment to master and control the passions. Hence education, which is calculated to discipline the instinctive movements of the heart and to assure the development of the will, is of the greatest importance. Unfortunately this sort of education has never been more neglected than it is in our day.

We instruct our children; our fathers educated theirs. We, at great expense, provide them with superficial and insufficient notions of grammar and the natural sciences, which teach them neither how to live well nor how to die well. Our fathers developed souls by carefully cultivating the good and repressing the evil inclinations with severity and by preserving the imagination from distractions.

This educational method is long and difficult, but it is indispensable. The incomparable masters who have laid down its rules, men like Fénelon,[3] Dupanloup,[4] etc., have made confidence and love the basis

[3] François de Salignac de la Mothe-Fénelon (1651–1715), Bishop of Cambrai, was renowned as an author and as a preacher. His *Explications des Maximes des Saints* (1696) was condemned in part by Pope Innocent XII (1699). Fénelon humbly submitted. By his mildness he brought back many Huguenots to the Mother Church. He defended the rights of the Church against Jansenism and Gallicanism.

[4] Félix Dupanloup (1802–1878) was Bishop of Orléans from 1849. He was distinguished for his eloquence and his pedagogical works. At the Vatican Council he at first sided with the opposition, but submitted to the decree of Infallibility.

of all education. By giving the child incessant evidence of sympathy and affection, we win his heart, mould him at leisure and make of him an honest man.

Love is the greatest means of education. We never refuse to obey him who loves us. On the other hand harshness and violence yield but poor results. "Fear," says Fénelon, "is like violent drugs, which are resorted to only in extreme diseases; they purge, but they change the temperament and exhaust the organs. A soul directed by fear is always weakened thereby." [5]

Let us hasten to add, however, that affection does not exclude respect; it presupposes it. The child must have as much submissiveness as confidence towards his teacher. The authority of the teacher and of the parents must be thoroughly established. Correction is but the necessary guarantee and the last resource of authority. There must be no hesitation in resorting to chastisement to punish grave faults or to subdue intractable natures. "Painful arguments" make more impression on the heart of the child than reasoning; they remain engraved upon his memory and discipline his will.

In the French senate he defended the freedom of academic instruction by the Church as well as the rights of the Apostolic See.

[5] *Traité de l'Éducation des Filles,* c. 5.

These necessary elements of education do not always suffice to develop the heart and to correct the innate vices of childhood. At times nature obstinately rebels against them; and medical science must come to the aid of moral hygiene. Delicate, nervous children have violent passions which resist persuasion as well as coercion; corporal punishment only exasperates them and may seriously endanger their health. The irritability of the nervous system is at times so great that the least constraint or the slightest reprimand suffices to evoke violent outbursts of anger or even delirium in one; attacks of weakness and sudden depression of the energies in another. If the disturbances are repeated, the attacks grow worse and eventually may lead to general debility and death. In such cases hygienic and medical treatment must be resorted to without delay.

Apart from these special and quasi-pathological cases, in which the instinct shows unusual strength and a vicious tendency, and the exercise of free will is impaired, the control of the passions, we need hardly remark, depends solely and entirely upon the will and is accomplished by Christian education.

The passions are subdued, yet they constantly revive with greater strength. By their very nature they remain intractable to reason and must be constantly watched and held in check. Their violence abates neither with age nor with the development of reason, but rather increases with the vigor of manhood, and the whole life of him who wishes to remain honest and wise is an incessant struggle with the instinctive and unregulated impulses of nature.

The moral hygiene of the adult is the same as that of the child. It does not suppress the passions, but restrains them, and subjects them to the control of the will. The will must be prepared early; it must be subjected to trials to give it self-reliance, and to exercise to develop and strengthen it: such is the object of education, and the end we must daily strive to attain.

A strong, upright will which adheres to duty is a salutary check to the passions; it simultaneously serves reason and safeguards the heart. Without it man is nothing, or at least he is not a *character*, *i. e.*, he lacks "that holy power of which he stands most in need," and the disappearance of which from modern society is so justly deplored by Lacordaire.[6]

It does not suffice, however, to merely restrain the passions; we must, in directing them along a normal way, also provide them with the necessary diversion. The best means to this end is work.

[6] Dominique Lacordaire (1802–1861), first a lawyer, then an enemy of the Church, then a priest and a monk, is a great ornament of the Dominican Order. His *Conférences,* given in the parish church df Notre Dame de Paris, were justly famous; in them he presented in a modern form the apologetic principles of St. Thomas of Aquin.

No matter how strong the will power may be, it would never be capable of sustaining us in the fulfillment of our duty if the sensibility did not receive a nourishment proportionate to its activity. "Idleness is the worst of counselors, a source of evil thoughts and temptations." [7] History proves that the greatest geniuses found in it the rock of perdition and death. "Solomon and Samson were holy as long as they were active; but as soon as they yielded to idleness, they were ruined," says St. Augustine. Work, on the other hand, possesses a superabundance of energy, which can be intensified at will by hygiene and moral teaching: it employs the mind, quiets the nerves, strengthens the organism, and constitutes the best protection against ennui and excesses.

Passion naturally tends to increase and to exaggerate in the presence of its object, owning neither bond nor master. Hatred, for instance, becomes more deeply rooted in the heart and grows more vehement and tenacious the more the object of resentment presents itself to vision or memory. The same is true of the other passions—anger, desire, love, etc.

All precautions are useless if we intentionally approach those objects which arouse or resuscitate

[7] St. Bernard, *De Med.*, Bk. I, c. IV: *"Omnium tentationum et cogitationum malarum sentina otiositas."*

our passions, if we offer to eager sensibility the means of exalting itself, of troubling our judgment, and of misleading us. Therefore, we must carefully flee the occasion, especially that which excites our dominant passion. Men who seek the occasion and then complain that they have become the slaves of their vices, are unreasonable. Nature, as such, inevitably obeys its instincts. How can carnal desire resist the sensual solicitations intentionally proffered by so many unfortunates? The flesh always responds to its purpose, whilst the blinded or perverse spirit but too frequently betrays its duty and God.

Certain violent passions which take entire possession of the soul and make it their plaything, not only demand a removal of the causes which awaken them, but also require necessary remedies. In this regard medical science offers valuable aid to moral hygiene. Its prescriptions, authoritatively formulated and obeyed to the letter, have preserved more than one unfortunate victim, whom mere counsels could not bring back to the path of virtue, from a lingering death or even from suicide.

The exciting passions, such as anger and despair, sometimes require an energetic treatment. Hydrotherapy often gives good results. The depressing passions, such as fear, shame, sorrow, are relieved by the cautious and graduated administration of various stimulants or tonics (alcohol, caffeine, etc.)

as well as by massage and hydrotherapy. Distraction, however, in all forms, is the best remedy; travelling especially performs miracles.

These means will not fail to triumph over the passions; but all would be useless if God did not crown our efforts with His grace. Between the clear perception of duty and its fulfillment lies an abyss which faith alone can span. Conscience is either religious or it does not exist at all. Religion, the foundation of morality, is the most solid rampart of the soul against the terrible and incessant assaults of the flesh.

# CHAPTER V

## MORTIFICATION

THE *old Adam* (*i. e., the flesh*), as we have seen, embraces soul and body and is the one great obstacle to our development, perfection, and eternal salvation. *Mortification* is the sovereign remedy recommended to us by the Church to repress our animal instincts and vices, to avoid and detest sin and, finally, to admit the grace of God to our souls. Hence mortification must be applied to our whole being, to both body and soul. On this point Bishop Gay, a learned and experienced theologian, says: "Mortification, while one in principle, has a double form and extends to a twofold object. It embraces the exterior as well as the interior man; and according as it is exercised upon one or the other, it is itself external or interior, corporal or spiritual. To mortify only a part of oneself, whether this be done intentionally or from cowardice, is merely wasting time. If the old man continues to live in us because our sensible appetites are not regulated (though our soul may, to a certain extent, remain honest) or, on the other hand, because the soul is given to avarice, or some similar vice, whilst the body is temperate and continent, it is eventually all the same. If in one way or other this sort of life reigns within us, the grace of Jesus Christ must of necessity die. Since in both cases we perform the works of the flesh, we ourselves become flesh, and a divine sentence excludes us from the Kingdom of God. St. Paul designates as "works of the flesh" not only the unregulated actions of the senses, but also hatred, jealousy, envy, idolatry, and everything which the badly controlled passions of the soul may inspire. And do you know to what our clear-sighted Augustine reduces the life of the flesh? He says that it essentially consists in living to oneself and for oneself, that is, that it lies entirely in the independence of the will and the egotism of the heart. Hence those are greatly mistaken who hold that mortification consists entirely or even principally in the affliction of the senses and in corporal penance. But no less do those deceive themselves who wish to reduce all mortification to the interior. This is one of the common errors of our times, and a very dangerous error, for be it by reason of that hypocrisy to which the world is more accustomed than it will admit, or by reason of an illusion which even Christians are not always able to escape, the pretension of which we are speaking usually conceals an actual and total abandonment of this indispensable duty; and even when this is not the case, it almost inevitably leads to the same thing by a gently descending path." [1]

Interior mortification, which affects the memory, the imagination, the sensibility, the heart, the mind, and especially the will, is evidently to be preferred to exterior mortification, not only because the soul is superior to the body, but also because the "flesh" is, to a certain extent, rooted in the soul. We shall not dwell upon this point, as it exceeds our competence.

Corporal must not be separated from spiritual mortification. The former is absolutely necessary in order that the latter may yield genuine fruits of sanctity. It is a divine obligation. The Church has ever taught its necessity and has imposed the exercise thereof upon all the faithful. The sobriety demanded by hygiene is a mortification, but—note this well— it is not yet Christian mortification. The use of the senses must be regulated not only according to the laws of nature, but also according to supernatural laws, and the measure of their true mortification is invariably completed by privation and suffering.

Every one of our senses must be mortified. The eye demands constant viligance, in order to preserve the soul from evil impressions. Are not the eyes the usual doors to sensuality? Hence we must safe-

[1] Gay, *De la Vie et des Vertus Chrétiennes,* 8th ed., II, pp. 20–21.

guard them against the sight of ignoble, dangerous, nay even vain and useless things. To guard one's eyes is to guard one's soul. The marvels of art are worthy of contemplation only in as far as they produce an ideal and raise us above perishable matter to the Supreme Beauty.

The ears should be shut not only to useless words, flattery, and the seductions of the world, to evil counsel and dishonorable proposals, but to all impressions that do not elevate the soul and fortify the heart. Within these wise limits it is not forbidden to listen to music and to enjoy its sweet harmonies. St. Augustine approves music for the church: "The spirit which still is weak," he says, "is raised to sentiments of piety by the delight which affects the ear." [2]

Mortification of the sense of smell demands the suppression of the pleasures which come to us through this channel. The Bishop of Hippo shows us how we can practice mortification of this sense by perfect indifference. "If agreeable odors are absent," he writes, "I do not seek them; if they are

[2] *Confessiones,* 1. X, c. 33. (This evidently applies to Church Music, *i. e.,* Gregorian and Cecilian, as well as to the best classical music. It certainly cannot apply to ragtime, jazz, etc., with their enervating, demoralizing influence, nor to the sensuous music of some of our operas. Hence we may apply to music also the words applied to masterpieces of art.—*Translator.*)

present, I do not reject them, though I am prepared to renounce them." [3]

To endure an offensive odor without complaint, and to suppress the instinctive repugnance of the sense of smell is a virtue. It is also a virtue to overcome the disgust and loathing which arise from fetid and nauseating odors. In this manner priests and physicians are called upon to mortify their sense of smell at the bedside of the sick and dying, and God thus gives them frequent occasions to exercise patience and acquire merit.

Taste is the sense which presides over nutrition; yet it is but one step from satiety to gourmandizing, and the mortification of this sense is especially necessary to keep us from sin. The Church has sought to guarantee this by two special practices, fasting and abstinence, which we shall study later. But in spite of all this, intemperance is one of the most widely disseminated vices and one of the hardest to eradicate.

We must eat to satisfy our hunger and to meet the requirements of the organism, but not to tickle the palate or to satiate an insatiable sensuality. Sometimes it is difficult to distinguish between a legitimate appetite and a factitious and evil craving of the palate. St. Augustine says: "If I proceed from the inconvenience of hunger to the relief provided by

[3] *Op. cit.*, l. X, c. 32.

eating, concupiscence, at this very point, lays an ambush for me; for this transition is accompanied by a sense of pleasure; nor can we arrive at this relief to which necessity obliges us in any other way. and although preservation of life is the only reason obliging us to eat and drink, this dangerous pleasure contravenes and seems, at first, but a servant following his master; but often he makes efforts to go ahead and finally to induce me to do for his sake what I had intended to do only from necessity. But necessity has not the same extension as pleasure, and often when there is enough for necessity, there is but little to satisfy pleasure. Often, too, we are uncertain as to whether it is the need of preserving life which prompts us to continue to eat, or whether it is the deceptive enchantment of pleasure that impels us." And the pious doctor concludes: "We must put a curb upon our appetite by a just observance of the golden mean between too much and too little." [4]

After quantity, the quality of nourishment most preoccupies sensualists, whereas it leaves the Christian soul indifferent. It is certainly proper to prescribe a substantial and nourishing diet in accordance with the laws of hygiene; but this rule by no means contradicts a properly understood mortification, since it does not concern itself with the odor or taste of foods, but only with their nutritive

[4] *Op. cit.,* l. X, c. 31.

value. Mortification requires indifference. To eat simply to gratify the taste is vain and dangerous. We should eat whatever is set before us, without predilection or repugnance, and we should have no preferred dish.

Many persons are tempted to advance yet further on the royal road of penance by selecting foods which are repugnant both to their tastes and their stomachs. Without censuring these, St. Francis de Sales prescribes this eminently wise rule: "There is more merit in eating all things with indifference than in always selecting the most disagreeable." [5] The reason he gives is that we thereby surrender even our choice. This rule is corroborated by a physiological argument which is not without importance. Hygiene teaches that the stomach revolts against certain foods and that it is as useless as it is painful to grow furious at its resistance. Not only is nutrition in no way benefited by undigested food, but the latter overtaxes the stomach, and thus causes torture and frequently danger.

Touch, the most extended of all the senses, is also the one most in need of mortification. Among the inconveniences that especially affect the flesh, are heat, cold, the weight and roughness of garments, hardness of the bed, and particularly those corporal penances which past centuries held in such

[5] *Introduction to a Devout Life,* Part III, c. XXIII.

high honor and which we somewhat neglect. These penances, which have produced saints and procured for many Christian souls superabundant merits and the gift of a pure life, will be studied from a medical and physiological viewpoint in our next chapter.

With the mortification of the senses it is necessary to combine numerous other practices which assure the supremacy of the soul over the body. The first of these is labor. There is nothing which more effectively subdues the flesh and more easily breaks its galling fetters than the fatigue which results from assiduous labor. Whether this labor be manual or purely mental, whether it engage the body or the mind, it has as an effect the subjugation of the senses, disciplines the passions, and preserves the freedom of the soul. "Much study," says Holy Writ, "is an affliction of the flesh" (Eccl. XII, 12). Manual labor distracts the mind and gives food to nervous activity.

No matter what the character of labor may be, it has its limits, and we must obey nature by giving a place in our daily routine to *rest,* which soothes the nerves and repairs the losses of the organism. But here again there is occasion for practicing mortification, in as far as it does not impair health. The right mean is not always easy to find, and hence, before engaging in such penances, it is necessary to consult both confessor and physician.

The amount of sleep which a person needs varies with age, sex, temperament, occupation, and other conditions. Broadly speaking we may say that seven to eight hours of sleep are necessary for adults. Sleep is a rigorous necessity of nature, and we must allow ourselves the necessary time for it, if we do not wish to become victims of loss of appetite, anæmia, debility, and especially neuroses (in the case of women). All directors of conscience know, that, as St. Francis de Sales says, "we must not crush the spirit by overtaxing the body," [6] and they all subscribe to the humorous directions which he one day sent to an overzealous nun: "To eat little, to work hard, to worry and deny the body its rest, is to expect great service from an emaciated horse which gets no feed." [7]

By reason of their severity, night watches were kept in a heroic manner by the saints, in imitation of the Divine Master; but they must not be permitted to every pious soul. Blessed were those whose health permitted such austerities! The majority of men to-day, with their shattered and weakened constitutions, must refrain from them. Those who wish to subject themselves to this severe test, must not depend upon their own judgment. Those who are sick, nervous, anæmic, or the simply delicate, the

[6] Letter to St. Frances de Chantal, Feb. 5, 1608.
[7] Letter to Mother Angelica of Port Royal, Sept. 2, 1619.

young, and those who have passed their sixtieth year, are absolutely forbidden to keep vigils.

Most men, even Christians, do not seek mortification, do not go forth to meet it, and do not understand its value. They do not wish to taste its sweet and fortifying savor. Yet sooner or later mortification comes to all in the guise of illness. "Sickness," says Bishop Gay, "is *the* great mortification. If the others are of silver, this one is of gold; for even if we ourselves have brought it on (disease originates in original and often in actual sin) yet in its higher aspect, and in as far as everything that happens depends upon God, it is a divine fabric. How just are its blows! How efficacious! How sickness, better than labor and voluntary penances, touches the very vitals of the old Adam, and, as it were, snatches us from ourselves! I dare say that patience in illness, especially protracted illness, is the masterpiece of mortification and constitutes the triumph of the mortified soul at death." [8]

This stern experience, which no one escapes, furnishes the patient with innumerable occasions of testing his virtue and of acquiring new and precious merits. Patience is not an easy matter for him who suffers. Obedience to the physician's orders is irksome, nay, at times cruel. Detachment from the world and sincere surrender to Divine Providence

[8] *Op. cit.,* p. 34.

are always heroic in him who is tormented by pain or about to die. The exercise of these beautiful virtues is as edifying as it is useful. It confers not only spiritual benefits, but also valuable corporal advantages. How much is not the task of the practitioner facilitated by submissiveness on the part of the patient! How many unexpected recoveries result from this disposition! Unfortunately even among Christians, sickness, that decisive test of sanctity, is not always borne without murmuring; and rare are those who can smile at pain and bless suffering. One of these, the mild Henri Perreyve, has depicted with a masterful hand the duties of the sick in his admirable book which Gratry calls "a true masterpiece blessed by God," and which we should like to see in every home.[9]

[9] *La Journée des Malades,* printed in many editions.

# CHAPTER VI

## PENANCE

MORTIFICATION, as we have seen, must embrace the whole man, body and soul. The *flesh* must be chastised, combated, and held in check. This is the first and necessary condition of a devout life, and the highest accomplishment of Christian asceticism. Evil proceeds from the "heart," but the senses actively coöperate in sin, and penance is vain unless the body is subjected to the soul. Hence the great Apostle St. Paul tells us that he chastises his body and brings it into subjection (1 Cor. IX. 7). But the practice which best assures this necessary servitude is *afflictive penance,* effected by appropriate instruments.

The most legendary of these instruments, and the least used at present, is the *haircloth* or *hairshirt,* which the ages of faith held in high esteem, and which for many was an effective means of sanctification. The *hairshirt* is a tight shirt of raw wool, worn next to the skin. The *haircloth* (*cilicium*) is a girdle made of the same material and worn in the same way. This means of maceration is very rigorous and its use must therefore always be authorized by some competent person; it is more or less prolonged and sometimes endures throughout life. When it can be endured without harm to the body, it is a powerful aid in conquering the assaults of concupiscence and conducting the soul to the highest degree of spirituality. Its action upon the skin being very irritating, it must be watched closely and, if necessary, absolutely forbidden to nervous, highly sensitive, or delicate persons and to those whose temperament predisposes them to cutaneous eruptions. A final danger of the hairshirt must be noted, namely, that its prolonged use makes it filthy and nauseous, and interferes with the essential functions of the skin. But this defect is not irremediable if the penitent has not contracted a lively affection for this blessed instrument of mortification and does not hesitate to separate himself from it, forgetting that perfection is inseparable from generous renunciation and total abnegation.[1]

A frequent penitential practice consists in wearing *bracelets* or *girdles of metal*. Whether they are

[1] If many of our young women would offer up to God the abnegations, pains, discomforts, which they suffer for the sake of fashion, and wore their uncomfortable shoes, clothing, etc., as mortifications instead of from vanity, many no doubt would become saints.—*Tr.*

[1] The use of the *cilicium* does not accord with our present knowledge of the sources of disease and of the ubiquity of disease germs. Not only must it have been a frequent cause of dermatitis and eczema, but also of boils and sometimes of

worn constantly or only for a time, for a few hours a day, or in temptations or trials, these instruments, provided with interior points, cause acute pain and suffering and are capable of procuring abundant fruits of mortification. They are as austere as the hairshirt and much more hygienic.[2] The reservations and dispensations indicated above are applicable to them also. In addition, persons authorized to make use of them must perform their penances *conscientiously* or submit to being supervised in a practice which often has a tendency to go to excess. If this kind of mortification is restricted to limits compatible with health and temperament, it is very useful, but if it is carried to excess, it has inconveniences and dangers. Hence, proper limitation of such penances is indispensable. They should be fixed by the confessor, aided by science; and it is the duty of the penitent to abide strictly and religiously by his decisions, absolutely surrendering his own will.

The *discipline* is the simplest, best known, and most widely used instrument of corporal penance.

carbuncles, which may in turn occasion deep and dangerous infections of important internal organs, a threat to health and to life to which no one, in the light of modern science has the right to expose himself.—Ed.

[2] The statement that "these instruments, provided with interior points" are "much more hygienic" than the *cilicium* is hardly accurate, since the breaks in the surface may easily furnish a port of entry for dangerous germs.—Ed.

Its purpose is to scourge the skin and it consists sometimes of a thin iron chain, sometimes of a knotted cord, sometimes of a simple prepared rod, or sharp metallic teeth. Most frequently it is merely a straight, flexible, and tough leather thong. This simple apparatus, if well managed, equals the most complicated of instruments for obtaining the purpose of mortification.

The *discipline* is intended to produce physical pain, to prolong the effects thereof in the body, to divert nervous perturbation into safer channels, to weaken the passions, to effect peace of mind and to sanctify the soul. It must be wielded slowly, or at least soberly, methodically, and upon certain parts of the body, taking care to change the afflicted portion from time to time. The usual points of attack are the shoulders, the back, the arms and forearms, the legs and thighs, and especially the posterior region. The chest must be spared, especially in the case of women, because the bruising of the breasts can be the occasion of serious injury. The back is, in general, very favorable, but it quickly swells and becomes sore if it is scourged to excess.

The act of scourging may last from ten minutes to one-half hour, more or less, according to the strength of the penitent; but it cannot be renewed every day without losing its force and, above all, without eventually disturbing the mental state. In general, it should be enjoined no oftener than two or three times a week, especially for Friday, the day when the remembrance of the scourging of Our Lord will serve as an encouragement to piety and as a salutary lesson. It is authorized, nay, even advised at the time of temptations or after serious faults. But recourse to it on private authority is forbidden.

The discipline must be regulated in its application to assure the desired moral results and not injure the health. If it is practiced with violence or precipitation, it exposes the penitent to attacks of weakness, palpitations of the heart, etc., and may lead to regrettable accidents. On the other hand, it is useless if applied gently and by an indolent hand. Prudence does not exclude rigor. Neither pain, nor bruises, nor drawing of blood are to be considered. Mortification would not be complete if the flesh were not injured so as to retain the imprints of the strokes of the discipline.

While all who aim at Christian perfection are called to the salutary rigor of this mortification, not all can bear it. It evidently exceeds the strength of many, and hence it should not be permitted to delicate and nervous persons except with great moderation and under close surveillance. The sick, especially those suffering from lung or heart trouble, must not be permitted the use of the discipline at all.

Finally, it is advisable to discourage the use of the discipline in the case of impressionable individuals, especially of emotional women distinguished by their exaltation, even though they appear to be in good health, as they may be affected by hysteria. This formidable affliction often causes anesthesia, in which its victims are insensible to pain. Hence scourging has not the intended effect upon them, but, on the contrary, seems to provoke strange and almost agreeable sensations, while at the same time it unduly excites the nervous system, which has already lost its normal inhibitions.[3]

Dr. Pruner, a famous German moralist and theologian, says: "Corporal mortifications have not their object in themselves, but are calculated to prepare the way, as much as possible, for a virtuous and conscientious exercise of the will and to promote a corresponding activity. . . . A certain indication that a person is practicing mortification entirely in the spirit of the Gospel, is a deep, interior peace, far removed from sullenness, gloom and caprice. Another characteristic is humble, self-sacrificing

[3] The following note is by Dr. Sleumer in the German translation of this work: "Since the discussion by Dr. Surbled in the original French is applicable rather to the Latin countries, this chapter has been abbreviated and adapted to the practical needs of German readers." We have retained Dr. Surbled's text, omitted by Dr. Sleumer, but added the latter's remarks, consisting largely of extracts from an article by Pruner in the *Kirchenlexikon.*—*Tr.*

charity towards one's fellowmen. The mortified Christian is as mild and indulgent towards others as he is severe with himself. Among pagans not yet enlightened by the Gospel we frequently meet with a self-torture intensified to a frenzy, amid extreme moral depravity. Among schismatic or heretical sects we discover a fanatical abandonment to corporal penances, as if these could replace every other means of grace and salvation, even the Sacraments. All this is but a confirmation of the truth that, outside the perfect dominion of the spirit of Jesus Christ, even the most ordinary truths and principles of morality are in danger of being caricatured, and that under the influence of the passions and of diabolical deception all good things degenerate.

"In order to make the body more willing to submit to the rule of the spirit and of divine love, many Christian souls may profitably have recourse to fasting, corporal penances, and vigils, but only under the following conditions: (1) These penances are to be permitted only in absolute obedience to the confessor and must never be left to the penitent's individual judgment. (2) The confessor must carefully watch that humility and contrition of heart and not spiritual pride and self-complacency are fostered by these practices. (3) Therefore these practices are, as a rule, not to be permitted as long as the soul is not earnestly willing to practice the absolutely necessary mortification of disputatiousness, obstinacy, irascibility, envy and loquacity. (4) In imposing and designing such austerities, the external circumstances as well as the moral condition of the penitent must be duly considered; for not everything is possible to everyone, nor is everything useful to everyone. (5) The adopted penitential practice must be persevered in, and not be changed or relinquished without sufficient cause. (6) To make this possible . . . it is advisable to impose but a light penance at first, and then gradually to progress to the more severe austerities. (7) The less extraordinary or peculiar a penitential practice is, and the more easily it can be employed in private and without the knowledge of others, the more it recommends itself." [4]

In a word, the essential thing in the life of self-denial demanded by Christian faith and in the penitential practices required for man's sanctification, is that he be equally on his guard against tepidity and excessive zeal and that he always observe the golden mean. All authors insist upon this point. True, the "flesh" must be crucified, not once, but constantly, in order that it may yield precedence to the spirit. But even though the soul must guide the body, it must not, under pain of losing the necessary services of the body and of provoking serious disorders, crush and exhaust it. If the body is weakened by privation

[4] J. E. Pruner, *Kirchenlexikon,* 2nd ed., Vol. I, c. 143.

and hardship, and robbed of its vitality, the return of the turbulent passions is apt to prove disastrous. We must adopt penitential practices with wisdom, and avoid abuses. It is best to adhere to the mild and discreet method of the incomparable St. Francis de Sales, who says: "Stags run badly at two seasons —when they are too fat, and when they are too lean. When the body is too much pampered and when it is too much weakened, we are greatly exposed to temptations, for the one makes the body insolent in its comfort, and the other makes it desperate in its discomfort; and even as we cannot carry it when it is too fat, so it cannot carry us when it is too lean." The same author concludes with the apt remark that, "generally, it is better to keep up our bodily strength more than is required, than to weaken it more than we need; for we can always reduce it when we will, but we cannot always restore it when we will." [5]

[5] *Introduction to a Devout Life,* Part III, c. 23.

# PART II

# THE NUTRITIVE LIFE

# CHAPTER I

## CONSTITUTION AND TEMPERAMENT [1]

LIFE in its development is uniform and fixed in its general characteristics, but varied in its forms. All men resemble each other in the nature of their organs, but each one is distinguished from the rest by the functioning of these organs. The vital activity is the same in all, but it has special modes of procedure. Physicians and hygienists must know how to discern these intimate differences, which are the result of the combined influence of heredity and environment in every individual; and it is precisely this differentiation which makes medical art a science. These differences cannot be reduced to a collection of physiological formulæ, but demand for their diagnosis a clear and sure judgment by means of which the physician is enabled to detect them and give proper advice to his patient.

[1] This entire chapter is rather out of date. A statement of the rôle of the physical part of man as a factor in his behavior might be written, but this would be a book in itself, to be written by a specialist, and sure to be at once attacked by all other specialists.—Ed.

Men have at all times assiduously studied the human organism with a view of obtaining a sound basis for a generally valid pathology, and many authors designate it indiscriminately by the words *constitution, nature,* or *temperament.* As a rule, however, the first two terms are used to designate a condition of strength; we say of one man that he has a "splendid constitution" and of another that he is a "weakling," according as his strength is developed or retarded. *Temperament,* strictly speaking, is a special mode of being, peculiar to the individual, which depends upon the difference of the proportions that exist between the various organs and systems (nervous system, circulatory system, etc.).

Temperament, therefore, is constituted by the preponderance in the organism of one system over others. When, for instance, in consequence of a natural or an acquired development, the nervous system predominates, the temperament is nervous; whereas, when the circulatory system predominates, it is called sanguine. By reason of these temperaments there is no satisfactory equilibrium and no perfect harmony in the body, and it is the task of hygiene and medical science to combat the excessive influence of any one system upon the others and to counterbalance it by favoring and developing the opposing qualities. Life, therefore, according to the theory which we are discussing, would present in its thousands of modes so many inequalities, defects, and sources of trouble and disorder that it would display neither poise nor harmony, and, if we be permitted to say so, it would confer little honor upon the soul as well as upon its Creator.

It must, however, be said that the typical or perfect temperament of the ancients (the *temperamentum temperatum* or *ad pondus* of Galen [2]) would be that in which all the elements of the organism, justly proportioned, would establish an exact equilibrium and mutually *temper* each other; perfect health would consist in the intimate and permanent harmony of the vital movements, in the balancing of all the powers of being. The temperament corresponding to each one's modality would therefore be a sign of inferiority, and the good health of which so many boast in the presence of unfortunate sufferers, would be a dream, an impossibility. "The best temperament," remarks Père Debreyne, "would be to have none at all, for then there would be a happy condition of perfect equilibrium among all organic actions." But it seems that this superior temperament—which really is no temperament at all—does not exist, and that perfect health is an ideal to which we may aspire, but which we can never attain.

[2] Claudius Galenus or Galen (born 130 A. D., died *circa* 200) was after Hippocrates the most noted physician of antiquity. He is the author of many scientific treatises.

Galen distinguishes four *temperaments:* the *sanguine,* the *choleric,* the *melancholy,* and the *phlegmatic.* This division, based upon the supposed preponderance of one of the four most important fluids then known to science, the blood, the gall, the black bile, and the phlegm, has survived the wreckage of the ancient medical systems. Only the phlegmatic temperament has collapsed with the "phlegm" which was supposed to be its cause, and its place has been taken by three new temperaments, namely: the *lymphatic,* the *nervous,* and the *erotic.* Not all authors, however, admit these different temperaments; many accept but two or three, whilst others increase the list by inventing "mixed temperaments," which we shall here attempt to enumerate: *nervous-sanguine, nervous-choleric* or *bilious, nervous-lymphatic, sanguine-muscular, sanguine-lymphatic, lymphatic-sanguine, choleric-* or *bilious-sanguine, sanguine-choleric* or *bilious, melancholic-sanguine, sanguine-melancholic, choleric-* or *bilious-melancholic, melancholic-choleric,* or *bilious,* and so forth.

This division is, however, vain and fantastic. It gradually developed from the inability to apply the original theory to each individual; but even the original theory cannot withstand a searching criticism. Temperaments so various and so vague lose all their trenchant characteristics, all their value; a person never knows where the one commences and the other ends.

What are we to conclude? Does temperament consist in the predominance of this or that organic system over the others? It is precisely this, that the most careful observation has not as yet been able to prove; we are reduced to ingenious suppositions. Béclard frankly says that "no one can ever furnish proof that the lymphatic system is more developed in the case of individuals who are ordinarily designated as lymphatics." [3] On the other hand, the relative predominance of the nervous or circulatory systems in nervous or sanguinary temperaments is by no means fully established; and in order to save the theory, certain physiologists have remarked that the circulatory apparatus must not be considered solely in its development, but also in the value of the blood which it contains. But the composition of the blood depends upon nutrition, and we also know that the nervous system plays an important rôle in the process of nutrition.

Are we, therefore, to conclude that the temperaments do not exist or that they have no tangible and evident reality? No one doubts their existence, but their explanation is insufficient, nay false; and hence we must unhesitatingly reject this explanation. The question has been obscured by the teachings of the

[3] *Traité Elémentaire de Physiologie Humaine,* p. 1229.

past and by the errors of materialism, and must be transported to the realm of facts and solved in the light of reason.

To-day no one thinks of reviving the old secretional or fluid theory, which inspired the theory of the temperaments. Is it not in plain contradiction with the facts? The *black bile,* among other things, is a lost and undiscoverable secretion; and nevertheless we admit a melancholy temperament. Many still accept it, who, as the learned Béclard says, do not notice "that it is only a nervous temperament which has its foundation in a pathological condition of the liver."

It will not be useless to remark that the organism of the body supports the contention of Galen in establishing a mutual relationship between the size of the organs and their higher functions. It is by no means difficult to refute the thesis of materialism. By rejecting its errors and by eliminating suppositions which have no foundation in fact, we shall discover the true nature of the temperaments.

On what distinguishing traits is the enumeration of the temperaments and their differences based? Béclard says, "on characteristics drawn from the affective dispositions, from the passions, and from the intellectual faculties," in other words, they are based solely on the state of the brain and the nervous life. Here undoubtedly is the root of the temperaments and the cause of their variety. The peculiarities of every living being are due to the special form impressed upon it by the nerves. "The life of man," writes Dr. Lacassagne, "is not in his blood; *it is all in his nervous system*. It is this which is the interior being, the only really modifiable and perfectible part of him, and the *changes of the nervous system consequently affect the rest of the human economy*." [4] Consider the various temperaments; each one of them can be traced to a special form of nervous activity. This, as we saw, has been conceded in the case of the choleric temperament; it can be maintained *a fortiori* of the melancholy temperament. And what is the lymphatic temperament but a condition of pronounced asthenia? The sanguine temperament is so vaguely defined that it must be divided into several classes; but they all bear the stamp of nervous excitability. The erotic temperament originates in the passions and has an obvious connection with the nerve centers; but a dangerous error must be corrected in regard to it.

From the various descriptions given of this temperament, it is clear that authors frequently confound it with a morbid condition, and a similar confusion obtains in regard to the other temperaments. A nervous disorder is frequently mistaken for a nervous temperament; anæmia and scrofula pass as a

[4] *Précis d'Hygiène Privée et Sociale*, p. 574.

lymphatic temperament; hypertrophy of the heart gives the illusion of a sanguine temperament, and so forth. If we remove from the characteristics ascribed to the various temperaments whatever is clearly traceable to pathological conditions, little or nothing will remain. Thus the erotic temperament, when reduced to its due proportions, seems to show no special characteristics, and hence has no justification. Exactly what does it reveal? Nothing more than sexual love; but this love is inborn in every human being, and no one is exempt from its impulses and excitations. Its absence, far from being a favorable indication, must be regarded as abnormal and morbid. Sexual love is the very condition of matrimony. Even celibacy derives its merit from it. In a word, we all possess the so-called erotic temperament, for we have all received the sexual instinct from Nature; but that instinct must be duly regulated by the will, and everyone knows that the will is powerless in this matter if it is not strengthened by a living faith.

The theory of the temperaments, as it has been handed down to us, involves another important consequence, which cannot escape the moralist. It exaggerates the influence of the body over the soul, and of the temperaments over the will, and thus leads man to excuse, nay, even to justify, his most grievous faults. True, it is maintained that all the temperaments are more or less capable of correction, and that it is the task of hygiene, education, and religion to mould them; but the door is always left open for "attenuating circumstances" by minimizing the undeniable rôle of free will. He to whom the physician has ascribed an erotic temperament, or who has convinced himself that he has it, has a diminished sense of duty and manifests little or no sorrow for his transgressions. If such a person falls, it is not *his* fault, but that of his temperament; if he relapses or fails to rise again after a fall, it is done unconsciously, and as a result of a fatal natural inclination. If, on the other hand, he is endowed with a lymphatic temperament, his good nature must bear the blame of his lack of energy, his weaknesses, and his lack of virtue; for the will, no matter how good it may be, cannot withstand "nature." And thus under the pretence of science is set up an easy-going and lax system of morality which everyone gladly accepts, practices, and recommends, but with which an upright conscience cannot content itself.

The resources of the will must not be underestimated. It is a faculty of the soul which must be trained by education. According to the degree of its development it is more or less strong, more or less master of the whole man; but it always exists, and even in the most debased souls it can be revived, become conscious of itself, and grow strong beneath the blows of misfortune or in consequence of a good example or a friendly word. We must emphasize this power, which is given to us to rule the passions and to preside over the cerebral life,— all the more since the temperaments which some wish to substitute for the will are rather obscure and less clearly defined. Science in this regard is a chaos of opinions and hypotheses which must be tested and clarified.

Authors admit that most men have an undetermined temperament affected by age, nutrition, habit, profession, mental proclivities, the passions, excesses, the climate, and a thousand other circumstances which may influence, modify or even change the temperaments. Would it not be much simpler to admit that the modes of activity are as varied as the individuals themselves and that there really cannot be two or three definite temperaments, to which all these forms can be reduced?

Even the development of one individual necessarily entails several temperaments because the forms of life vary with age. In youth the lymphatic system assumes an importance which it later on loses. Are we to conclude from this that all children have a lymphatic temperament? The young man whose nerves are strong sees how his "temperament" is altered by the influence of a good education. A vicious life has just the opposite effect. But in both cases the temperament changes quite naturally with advancing age.

What shall we say of the exaggerated influence attributed to climate? For many the sun is not only the beneficent king of light and heat, but also the motive power of organic functioning and the principle of existence; nay, it is even supposed to create the temperaments. We are told that the nervous temperament is peculiar to the South and the sanguine temperament to the North. England and Holland are supposed to owe their lymphatic temperament to fogs and dampness. All the world accepts this aphorism, and yet it is but a gross paradox, in no wise confirmed by experience. Where do we find more indolent, more "lymphatic" characters than under the hot sun of Spain? What nation is more industrious, more active than that of cold England? And how many Frenchmen by no means merit the epithet "hothead," so benevolently bestowed upon them, and how many Flemings are characterized by energy and vivacity? The influence of environment can never explain the differences of the nervous temperament presented by individuals.

In a word, according to the present state of scientific research, "temperament" is only a hypothesis and not a certainty; it is a word that is supposed to designate the peculiar nature of each individual human being. It would be dangerous, therefore, to seek in it a basis for the direction of conduct or for therapeutics. The modalities of our being, of which so little is known as yet, are all connected with nerve life, which finds a check capable of controlling the passions and maintaining the necessary harmony between body and soul in the will.[5]

[5] In the latest English work on the subject, *Temperament: A Survey of Psychological Theories* (London, 1928), Miss Constance Bloor defines temperament generally as "the sum of the effects upon the mental life of the metabolic changes that are constantly going on in all the tissues of the body," and takes into account the speed with which these changes take effect and the time they last. In her concluding chapter, and an appendix, she discusses the possible uses of a scientific theory of temperament (if one existed, which she denies) from the point of view of education and mentions some ways in which teachers might measure differences of temperament among their pupils, *e. g.,* their varying distractability and the time taken to return to equilibrium. In the course of her treatise, which really does not take us much farther than Dr. Surbled's chapter written a generation ago, she quotes Dr. Berman's definition of temperament as "the grand intravisceral barometer" and Dr. Watson's statement that "some day we shall have hospitals devoted to helping us change our personality as easily as we can change the shape of the nose, only it takes more time." This is a manifest exaggeration, but it shows how far we are removed from the determinism that ruled the non-Catholic world in Dr. Surbled's day.—Ed.

# CHAPTER II

In order to live it is not sufficient to merely wish to be healthy; we must also understand and apply the means of preserving health. There is an art of living, and this art is taught by hygiene, the humble handmaid of morality.

The nutritive life must be regulated so as to insure the development of a being and the regular exercise of its organic functions. The methodical and rational use of food, and, in fact, of all those things that contribute to life in general, constitutes *diet*. It is an essential part of hygiene, and unfortunately the least observed.

A man must be temperate. He should eat only when he feels hungry and only enough to replenish his strength. The stomach has but a limited capacity, and what it does not digest, becomes for it a burden, a cause of fatigue, a source of danger. Overeating causes indigestion and its consequences. If we guard ourselves against confounding the appetite of the palate with that of the stomach, if we do not consider as a necessity of the body that which is merely a pleasure of the taste, we can be sure of fulfilling the law of temperance and of meeting the demands of nutrition. There is in this the further advantage that we do not overtax the organs and thereby avoid that train of diseases which proceeds from intemperance. *"He who is temperate in eating, is his own physician"* (*"Modicus cibi, medicus sibi"*) is a proverb embodying the wisdom of the ancients. If we eat moderately, we take the best possible safeguard for insuring our health.

Moderate eating, however, is not sufficient to constitute a good diet; the food we eat must also be suitable for the stomach. General rules can hardly be made in this regard, for the kind of food must be adapted to the physical states, nay, even to the habits of individuals. In order to regulate nutrition, we must not only consult taste and appetite, but also the idiosyncrasies of the stomach. The best food is that which is most digestible. On the other hand, if our stomach has an aversion to certain foods, and we insist on eating them, the revolt will be painful and fatiguing. Everyone knows his own stomach best, its aversions and preferences, its longings and caprices. Everyone should choose the foods that agree with him and avoid those that do not, and abstain entirely from those that cause discomfiture and derangement of the stomach.[1]

[1] Cfr. Surbled, *Hygiène pour Tous,* p. 85.

But the ability of the "stomach," or rather of the digestive system as a whole, to deal with the food is not the only nor the most important factor in determining the choice of a proper dietary. Equally to be considered are the condition of the kidneys, the metabolic tendencies of the tissues, by which is meant the intimate internal chemistry of the cells, having to do with the storing of fat, sugar, etc., and the possession of certain "sensitizations," or fondness for one or another article of food.

As eating has but one purpose, *i. e.*, the proper nutrition of the body, it is important that we partake of nourishing and assimilable foods in small quantities and under favorable conditions. We must not only eat but little, we must also eat in the right way. Treatises on hygiene give food values and furnish all the necessary data for a proper diet; and to these we refer the reader, contenting ourselves with a statement of the physiological laws that govern human nutrition.

Nourishment is obtained in general from substances derived from the animal and vegetable kingdoms: bread and meat, milk and vegetables, etc. Are we to conclude from this that our diet must be mixed, and that man, unlike most animals, is neither exclusively carnivorous nor exclusively herbivorous? This question has long been discussed by scientists and at last found its solution.

It is incontestible that a diet consisting exclusively either of vegetables or of flesh, suffices to sustain life. Experience proves that a flesh diet is better suited to the needs of the human organism than a vegetable diet and that man is carnivorous rather than herbivorous. Haller long ago remarked that a purely vegetable diet, if continued for many years or during a whole life-time, perceptibly weakens a man's strength and diminishes his muscular energy. A peculiar experience at the forges of Tarn confirms this observation of the learned physiologist. The smiths, who received only vegetable food, lost fifteen days each per annum by reason of fatigue and sickness. When, in 1833, a new manager changed the diet of the men and introduced flesh meat, the average loss of work per laborer was only three days per annum.

The insufficiency or inferiority of a purely vegetable diet is attributable to lack of nitrogen. Since this element is indispensable for the preservation of animal tissue, of the nerves and muscles, it follows that herbivorous animals have to balance the small proportion of nitrogen substances by the consumption of an enormous amount of nourishment. For this purpose nature has endowed them with a highly developed alimentary canal. It has been calculated that such an animal daily consumes a quantity of nourishment amounting to one-tenth of its total weight, whilst the carnivora do not consume more than one-thirtieth of their weight. By reason of his physical constitution, by his tooth formation and the construction of his alimentary canal, man occupies a middle position between these two extremes, which means that he can adopt either or both diets according to his good pleasure. If, however, he wishes to content himself with a vegetable diet, he must consume a disproportionately large quantity of food, so much so that the assimilation thereof by the body is effected but slowly, may frequently become difficult and even impossible; the organs become fatigued and deteriorate, and finally the system is overcome by weakness and debility.

A diet suitable for health varies according to the race and geographical position of man. Thus the Japanese can exist on a quantity of rice which a European stomach cannot digest, while the Esquimaux maintain excellent health on an exclusive diet of meat and fat. The European and American requires a mixed diet.

In spite of the teachings of science, some authors consider a meat diet as the source of "all the ills that flesh is heir to," whilst they regard the purely vegetable diet as a universal panacea and the primitive and normal diet, which alone harmonizes with moral teaching and hygiene, and therefore, alone insures health. These exaggerations of the *vegetarians* may lead some minds astray, but cannot change the laws of nature. Plants occupy a well-deserved place in our diet; but they should not, as we have seen, constitute our sole form of nourishment, lest the system be weakened. Hence, plant food must be combined with strongly nitrogenous foods, so that they may form a nutriment which is as constructive as it is vivifying. This is the fundamental requisite of every good diet.

Man, therefore, must observe a mixed diet, in which flesh and vegetables have their due proportions; the nitrogenous and carbohydrate elements must be balanced. The former are calculated to preserve and repair the organism and especially the muscular tissues and nerve fibers, which are so quickly worn out by the exercise of animal life; the latter contribute to the processes of oxidation and respiration and preserve the animal heat, all coöperate in vital activity. A *mixed diet* is especially necessary for laborers, and since labor is the law of human nature, we can conclude together with experience and physiology that man is essentially *omnivorous*.

# CHAPTER III

To observe *abstinence,* or to *refrain from eating meat,* as prescribed by the laws of the Church, means the abstention from flesh meat on all the Fridays of the year (except when a holyday of obligation falls on a Friday or other day of abstinence) as well as on certain *vigils, on the Ember days and the Wednesdays and Fridays of Lent* (this latter is for the United States by special indult. The general law of the Church commands the Fridays and Saturdays of Lent as days of abstinence). The law of abstinence is based on excellent moral reasons, and receives the full approbation of physiology. It has always been held in high honor by Christian nations, but is by no means peculiar to them alone.

Pagan antiquity was acquainted with abstinence, and sometimes practiced it more strictly than we do. Epictetus reduced his whole ethical doctrine to the famous formula: *"Abstine et sustine."* The disciples of Pythagoras renounced the use of flesh meat. The entire Orient strictly observed the law of abstinence, which was Mosaic before it became

Christian, and has remained uninterruptedly in force among the Mohammedans.

The idea of mortification and expiation certainly inspired this command and gained recognition for it in the whole world; but the doctrine was and is by no means unknown to medical science, which seeks rather to prevent than to cure disease, and has justly recognized abstinence from rich food as one of the most efficacious means at the disposal of hygiene.

Abstinence, then, is a valuable penitential practice for combating carnal desires and insures the dominion of the soul over the body, promotes physical health, and forms a valuable aid in therapy. Moralists and physicians agree in acknowledging the advantages of abstinence and recommending its practice; and therefore, it is one of the most surprising spectacles of our day to see how some families neglect this precept, whereas others understand and practice it.

Abstinence must be observed because it is a commandment of the Church; this principle, which dominates all, pervades the whole Christian life. Other reasons support it and convince us of its great value, but it alone must suffice to guide us and move us to obedience.

The Lenten diet is extremely varied, and embraces many appetizing and agreeable foods. Nevertheless, the food which forms its basis, namely fish, must be prepared in a very elaborate manner, in order that it may lose its natural unpalatableness, and yet never presents to the palate that savor which a good piece of meat offers. It is indeed true 'that in regard to foods, as in regard to colors, tastes differ widely, and that some persons consider exquisite what others reject as unpalatable and even nauseating. But even though we were willing to concede (what to us seems doubtful) the equality of a flesh and a vegetable diet, abstinence would still retain the character of its undeniable rigor, and would impart even to the best foods a bitter aftertaste. The obligation of observing the law of abstinence on certain days unquestionably is a real inconvenience, for mortification affects not so much the palate as the will.

While the social position of a person does not in itself alter the law of the Church, and in no respect curtails its binding power, greater or less affluence gives a different significance to the renunciation of flesh foods, and hence the sacrifice entailed by obedience has a very unequal value. The practice of abstinence, especially in the cities, is a little more expensive than the use of meat; and as there is no such thing as "small" expenditures for the poorer classes, they have to bear the whole burden of the renunciation which is enjoined, whereas the rich

do not always understand its significance or feel
its severity; [1] many, in fact, lose sight of it altogether,
since the days of abstinence are the days on which
the menu is the most select and dainty. Is not this
equivalent to observing the letter of the law and
to some extent disregarding its spirit?

The law of abstinence, which from time to time
interrupts our animal diet, is well adapted to the
requirements of the human organism. It would be
erroneous, as we have intimated before, to consider
man as exclusively *herbivorous* or exclusively *carnivorous*. He is essentially *omnivorous* by reason of
his physical constitution, and consequently a mixed
diet has greater value for him than for any other
living creature. Right here it is pertinent to protest
against the exaggerations of those who proclaim
an exclusively vegetable diet as the only correct
one.

The writers who favor an exclusively animal diet
are for the most part apostles of materialism, who,
because they hate the faith, represent man as *"a
stomach served by various organs."* Those who favor an exclusive vegetable diet are idealists, who
see in *vegetarianism* the principle of life and the
source of all virtues. Truth compels us to guard
against both extremes and to defend against both
the intimate and necessary connection which exists

[1] *Pastor Hermæ,* Bk. III, Sim. V. especially c. iii.

between the laws of the Church and the principles of physiology.

We need not here refute the claims of *vegetarianism,* for this system is condemned by science. The vegetarians do not cease to laud the merits of their theory and hold in all sincerity that habitual abstention from flesh meat improves the character, calms the passions, and confers innocence and virtue. To believe their statements, those who eat meat are ferocious and vicious barbarians, so that one could say: *"Tell me what you eat, and I will tell you what you are."*

Does not this agree exactly with the coarse statement of Feuerbach that "Man is what he eats"? [2] The most outspoken materialists seem, in this regard, to be of one opinion with the most exaggerated spiritualists, who live exclusively on fruit, grain, and roots. Moleschott, a learned atheist, attributes very astonishing effects to a vegetarian diet. "The nations," he says, "who principally live on a vegetable diet, are easily conquered by those who eat flesh meat." Accordingly, will-power, courage, and strength depend absolutely on the diet, and it is diet which governs the development of nations and regulates the destinies of empires. The founders of the ancient religions had an inkling of this great discovery and invented abstinence with good reason.

[2] *"Der Mensch ist, was er isst."*

They wished to produce in their followers a weakening of the will and thus obtain passive obedience. Behold the real results of materialistic science! We shall not honor them with a discussion, since we can count upon the good sense of our readers to condemn them.

The physiological value of abstinence foods is comparable to that of flesh foods; the former contain, in general, less nitrogen, but are richer in carbon. Fish does not differ much in composition from flesh meat. It is a little more aqueous and consequently lighter. But this is not the place to undertake a comparative study of foods.[3]

What experience as well as physiology has established, is that an abstinence diet, which is energy building rather than tissue building, is especially adapted to warm climates, where organic expenditure is but small. In the Orient, in Asia and Africa, in fact, in the entire torrid zone, the natives content themselves with an almost purely vegetarian diet (fruits, vegetables, grain, milk, etc.). Flesh meat is rarely eaten, not only because it is difficult to obtain and preserve, but also because it is not indispensable for the needs of the organism in those regions.

In the temperate zones a mixed diet is necessary for good health. The proportion of vegetable and

[3] Cfr. our *Hygiène pour Tous*.

animal food required by each depends upon the nature of his work. Brain workers as a rule require food with a high energy content, in a relatively small bulk such as meat. Farmers, on the other hand, who live out in the open air and have to work long hours only during the agreeable seasons, find the best guarantee of good health in their living conditions. They are not, however, as has been frequently asserted, given to a purely vegetarian diet, and though many of them eat little or no fresh meat, all consume much lard, salted pork, and bacon. Hence their diet may be called abundant and substantial rather than frugal.

With the charity which she has received from her Divine Founder, the Church has always tempered rigor with mildness in the application of her disciplinary laws. Thus she imposes no obligation of abstinence upon the sick or convalescent, especially if the physician declares that a light meat diet would hasten recovery. If a person is healthy, she takes into consideration his age [4] and occupation. Therefore she grants ample dispensations, especially during Lent, to laborers, mothers, teachers, and physicians, in a word, to all who are steadily engaged in hard labor. Weak and delicate natures have a right to similar consideration. On a physician's advice or prescription the confessor will permit

[4] The aged are not strictly bound to abstain.

the use of flesh meat.[5] It may not be out of place here to remark that the advice given by a physician burdens his own conscience, and that he may prohibit abstinence only for grave reasons.

The Church also takes into consideration the needs of the poor, and in many dioceses, *e. g.,* of Germany and Mexico, permits them the use of flesh meat on all days, with the sole exception of Good Friday. A similar dispensation is granted to sailors and soldiers in active service.[6]

[5] In some dioceses the faithful may act according to the prescription of a concientious physician without recourse to the confessor. (Dr. Sleumer in a footnote of his German translation of Surbled's work, *Die Moral,* 3rd ed., p. 56.)

[6] Those civilians who belong to the common household of soldiers, as a rule participate in the above-mentioned mitigation of the law of abstinence. Everyone should guide himself by the Lenten regulations of his own diocese (Dr. Sleumer, p. 56).

# CHAPTER IV

## FASTING

FASTING is essentially a religious practice, and consists in abstaining from food in a spirit of mortification and penance. This practice is of great antiquity. It was observed by the Greeks and the Romans, and forms a component part of the Old as well as of the New Law. We shall here consider only the law of fasting prescribed by the Catholic Church for the *Ember Days,* certain *vigils,* and *the forty days of Lent.*

The *strict* or *"black"* fast, *i. e.,* complete abstinence from all food, is not prescribed, but many fervent Christians (*e. g.,* in monasteries and convents), assume it freely.

The *ordinary* or *mitigated* fast, which the Church prescribes for all the faithful, consists of one full meal and a collation, both consisting of abstinence foods.[1] Children, adolescents up to the completed

[1] In former times this was a general prescription. Further concesssions on the part of the Church now permit the "use of flesh meat" at the *principal meal* in many dioceses. *Complete abstinence,* however, is still prescribed for the Fridays of the year, Ash Wednesday, Holy Thursday (not in the United

85

twenty-first year, as well as persons over sixty years of age, are dispensed from fasting. Numerous other dispensations temper the rigor of the fast still more. But before speaking of them we must consider fasting from a physiological and medical point of view.

Of all the truths brought to our attention by observation and common sense, none is more evident than this, that we must eat in order to live. Though food constitutes a necessity of nature, the amount required is extremely variable. Some need abundant nourishment even when they are at leisure, whereas others are satisfied with little in spite of hard work. This matter is decided by temperament and especially by habit. But no matter how little food is consumed, a certain quantity is absolutely necessary for the organism to maintain its life and to replenish its strength. And yet science answers the question, "Can we live without eating?" in the affirmative, because one who is subjected to voluntary or forcible abstinence from all food, becomes *autophagous, i. e.,* sustains himself on his own bodily substance for some time. William Granié, of Toulouse, having been condemned to death, preferred suicide to the scaffold and died after refusing all food

States), and Good Friday. The use of fish and flesh meat at the same meal is permitted under the New Code of Canon Law, which went into effect on Pentecost, 1918. The permission to take a "little bread" in the morning is of comparatively recent date. (Dr. Sleumer).

for forty days. Dr. Tanner survived a fast of forty-five days. Viterbi, an attorney, who was condemned to death in 1821, adopted the same method, but lived only eighteen days. The physician and philosopher Hufeland reports the case of a man who, being disgusted with life, decided to die of hunger. September 15, 1818, he retired to a lonely copse and died there, literally starved to death at the end of eighteen days, October 3. He had the melancholy courage to record the painful sufferings which he endured day after day. His notes cease on September 29. The comparatively rapid death of this man must not, however, be attributed to hunger alone, as changes in the weather, cold and exposure entered as contributing factors into the case.

These facts, as well as many others noted by science, prove the possibility of prolonged fasting. But they were long unknown to the public or were considered as fabulous or improbable, and it is only of late years that the experiments of Tanner, Succi, and others have decisively proved that want of food injures neither life nor the activity of the senses, nay, not even reason, but only entails a progressive loss of weight, the result of the wasting of the organism. Such abstinence from food as a rule does not include *the renunciation of water*.[2] A patient who

[2] The supervision of these voluntary "fasters" was so vigilant, both day and night, that no deception was possible,

would be deprived of both food and water could not live longer than ten or fifteen days. Water constitutes two-thirds of the total weight of the body and is absolutely necessary for the circulation of the blood and the ordinary processes of metabolism. Hence, the use of liquids which contain no dissolved nutriment (as is the case with milk, chocolate, broths, strong beer, etc.) does not break the ecclesiastical fast.

Such, then, is the solidly established result of the sensational experiments which engaged public attention for many years. The ecclesiastical law of fasting finds in them a support which is all the more valuable as these "fasters" did not intend to furnish it.

The power of the organism to resist abstinence from food is not the same in all individuals, but depends upon various causes. One of the most evident of these causes is the difference of climate. Everyone knows that man sustains the lack of food with difficulty in cold countries. A warm climate, on the contrary, is favorable to the practice of fasting, because it reduces the organic wastage of the body to

especially since frequent medical examinations were made. The "faster" is confined in a glass case, which stands in the middle of a large room. Before he enters, he has received the predetermined amount of water. A stove gives him the necessary heat. The windows of the glass house are closed on all sides and sealed. Visitors have free access to the place at all times. (Dr. Sleumer).

a minimum. We must, furthermore, not lose sight of the fact that abstinence is rendered easier by habits of sobriety. The people of the Orient, for example, stand excessive and prolonged fasts without fatigue.

Women are less capable of resisting lack of food than men. Age produces the greatest differences in this regard. In a general famine the young succumb first. Dante took this scientifically established fact into consideration when he let Gaddo, the youngest son of Count Ugolino, die first on the fourth day of enforced hunger. Extreme old age, too, imperiously demands regular nourishment, little though it may be, and cannot long resist a strict fast.

The influence of temperament is no less evident. Under identical conditions some persons, thanks to their natural qualities, can endure a protracted fast far better than others of the same age. The reasons for this difference are not easily discoverable. Delicate, anæmic persons quickly succumb. Nervous temperaments, however, distinguish themselves above all others by a remarkable aptitude in this direction. An energetic will, supported by a well developed and active nervous system, is capable of most enduring resistance. This can be seen from the cases of suicide mentioned above, as also from the experiments of the "fasters."

If a nervous disposition is favorable to abstention

from food in the normal state, it becomes much more so in a pathological state. Neurotics exhibit a peculiar aptitude for fasting. Hysterics, lethargics, and cataleptics frequently live a long time without food. Their condition is, in many respects, similar to that of animals during hibernation. We need hardly remark that such manifestations occur almost exclusively in females.

Habit, as we have noted before, is one of the causes which explain the greater or less resistance to hunger. A stomach which is used to a light diet, will more easily sustain abstinence than one which is accustomed to abundant food. Here, perhaps, may be found the solution of a difficulty which frequently puzzles people—how it is that, whilst religious can bear frequent fasting without injury to their health, those who eat much are incapable of sustaining the smallest deprivation of food and do not know how to submit to ecclesiastical laws. They do not wish to understand that sobriety and temperance are the preparation and the only practical means of faithfully observing the law of fasting.

For the rest, the ecclesiastical authorities freely grant dispensations from fasting, whenever occupation or condition of health demands it. The physician, who is frequently consulted on this point, must act according to his conscience. The law of fasting must be modified for those who are fatigued and obliged to perform hard and constant labor. Fasting must be prohibited not only to the sick, but also to delicate persons, to anæmics, to convalescents of every description, to pregnant women, to those suckling their babes, etc.

# CHAPTER V

## THE EUCHARISTIC FAST AND COMMUNION OF THE SICK

THE *Eucharistic fast* is the strict fast imposed by the Church upon those who wish to receive Holy Communion. He who wishes to receive into his body the adorable Body of Jesus Christ, must neither eat nor drink anything from midnight on. This regulation, whose appropriateness needs no proof, in general entails no notable hardship for the faithful, since they usually communicate at the early Masses. It is a little severe only for priests who must celebrate a late Mass.[1] This law admits of an exception only in the case of severe illness. In certain cases it can be suspended by papal dispensation; but of this we need not speak.

[1] By a Decree of the Holy Office, March 22, 1923, Ordinaries are instructed that they may obtain from the Sacred Congregation either an indult for individual priests or else a faculty allowing them regularly to dispense from the ecclesiastical fast after the first Mass in case of bination, or in any other case where the same cannot be observed without grave risk of ill-health or weakness as the result of strain. In all cases the concession is restricted to liquid food, and excludes intoxicating liquors (*Eccl. Rev.* June, 1923).—*Tr.*

If Holy Communion is administered to a person in danger of death, it bears the sweet and beautiful name of *Viaticum* (*i. e.,* provision for a journey). It fortifies the recipient against the temptations of the last hour and grants him the necessary strength for the journey to eternity. It is the Master's last visit in this life, at which He grants the aid of His omnipotence and, as it were, gives a pledge of His mercy. Who would wish to be deprived of this infinite consolation at a moment when all abandon him, and who would not try to procure this solace for others? Hence the Church by her doctrine as well as by the mouth of her theologians permits the reception of Holy Communion without the Eucharistic fast whenever there is danger of death.

If the illness is prolonged and the danger of death constant, can the patient communicate from time to time by way of *Viaticum?*

This question was at one time debated, some maintaining that the favors of the Church must not be abused, whilst others defended a more lenient opinion, by taking into consideration the unavoidable evils of disease and maintaining that both body and soul must participate in the priceless graces of Holy Communion unto the end.

It is beyond all question that the law of the Eucharistic fast is very wise and should be suspended for grave reasons only. The body must prepare itself just like the soul to receive Our Lord. That the Eucharistic Bread ought not be exposed to the least contamination before it is dissolved, is not and cannot be a matter of indifference to a true Christian heart. Fortunately, the difficulty is not insurmountable.

The dying Christian who asks for the Viaticum hardly takes any more "food," but his fevered mouth incessantly craves for a drink, his dry lips want to be moistened and his weak stomach demands cordials and tonics. The strict fast would be most arduous for him, and might perhaps hasten his death. Should we, then, neglect the care of his body, whilst we respond to the cry of his soul? Should we deny him a spoonful of liquid, a few drops of sugared water or of wine, when, besides these palliatives, he desires the Bread of the strong? Can we really oblige him to choose between the weak consolation which the now impotent physician offers, and that divine help which the Great Physician is ready to give him?

On the one hand, the temporal interests of the dying are precious and worthy of consideration, whilst on the other hand, Catholic doctrine must be safeguarded. The Church, however, finds a means of reconciling both demands. She allows the severity of her discipline to yield to the spiritual welfare of the sick, and permits Holy Communion to be administered frequently as Viaticum. She also allows the sick to drink, in order to facilitate the swallowing of the Host, and finally permits the breaking of the Sacred Host, for the priest may, at his discretion, give the sick person a very small and quickly soluble and assimilable particle of the same.

This latter practice, which seems to us to solve all ordinary difficulties, is also in order when a disease of the face or tongue or mouth (*e. g.*, cancer) or rigidity of the masseter muscles prevents free access to the interior of the mouth, and there is danger that the Host may be lost or dissolved before it is swallowed.

A small particle placed in the most accessible passage of the digestive tract, runs no risk of being lost, and constitutes the best safeguard for the dying person. If the upper approaches are entirely closed, the piety and ingenuity of the physician or of the priest will discover some other means to make the reception of the Holy Viaticum possible. In this regard we know of nothing more touching or more worthy of imitation than the pious zeal of St. Frances de Chantal, of which her learned biographer, Bishop Bougaud, gives us an account.[2] A frightful cancer had eaten away the whole of a young woman's face. Madame de Chantal nursed the poor woman, who had been deserted by everyone, even by her husband. "After the disease had robbed the maxillary bones of their flesh and bared the teeth, the disease pro-

[2] Bougaud, *Histoire de Ste. Chantal,* Vol. I, pp. 275–277.

gressed, on the one hand, to the ears, and on the other, down to the chin, so that the countenance of the woman would have resembled a skull, had not the eyes, which rolled in their fleshless sockets, made it even more horrible. . . . The cancer progressed so rapidly that, after it had detached the maxillaries, a hole appeared deep down in the esophagus. Through this opening St. Frances fed the patient with an instrument, which she had caused to be made especially for this purpose. The poor sufferer could no longer pronounce a single word. Her breath came in pitiful gasps from this opening. It was a spectacle to cause the bravest to quail. When death came she had but one regret, namely, that she could not receive Communion. Madame de Chantal read this regret of the poor patient in her eyes, and since she desired to care for her soul no less than for her body, she persuaded the pastor to give the patient a tiny particle of the Sacred Host through the hole in the esophagus by means of a little silver fork, made especially for this purpose. The poor woman died quietly and with Christian resignation about a quarter of an hour after this happy Communion."

If in consequence of swelling which has affected the tongue, the pharynx, or the esophagus, there is no other way to the stomach, may a tube be used to convey the Sacred Host? We have no doubt that it may. When the swelling more or less completely bars the entrance to the pharynx, or when it is impossible to swallow and no tube gives access to the stomach, Holy Communion could evidently not be administered without great imprudence. In such a case it is proper to counsel the unfortunate patient to make an act of intense and fervent spiritual Communion, to replace the real Communion of which disease deprives him.

The most varied cases may occur in practice; but they will never offer serious difficulties if we consider them in the double light of reason and faith. Faithful to the words of her Divine Founder, the Church wishes Holy Communion to be given as a food (*per modum cibi*). Now the stomach is the principal organ for the reception and digestion of food. The reception of Holy Communion will, therefore, be possible in every case where ordinary food can reach the stomach, either in the natural way or by a medical or surgical device.

# CHAPTER VI

## INTEMPERANCE

INTEMPERANCE or *gluttony* is, perhaps, the most widespread of all vices. This vice degrades man and is very disastrous both to the individual and to society. We cannot censure it severely enough, nor can we strive too zealously and perseveringly to eradicate it. By the fact that the Church designates the unregulated use of food and drink as a *capital sin,* she serves not only the interests of morality, but also supports with her great authority the precepts of hygiene and renders a signal service to civilization. The doctrines of the Church, which embrace all the duties of man, have long anticipated the condemnation pronounced upon intemperance by science; they have admirably expressed the close relationship existing between nature and morality, between the body and the soul.

By virtue of the intimate mutual relations which unite all the component parts of our being, not only are reason and the affections obliterated and degraded by intemperance, but the whole system is altered and health destroyed. The vice of intemperance with fatal certainty leads to the collapse of the spirit and the decay of the body; it destroys the will and vital activity. We must study it in the two forms in which it manifests itself, *i. e.,* excess in eating and excess in drinking. In the former case the vice is called gluttony, in the second, drunkenness.

Food must satisfy the cravings of hunger and restore the wasted energy of the body. If this object is not attained, the diet is insufficient; if it exceeds the proper limit, it is excessive and dangerous. Now, either by reason of the violent stimulus of a never sated sensual craving, or by reason of an almost unconquerable habit, men have an unfortunate tendency to overindulge in eating. All pathology bears witness to this, and the various diseases of the stomach prove that the greedy palate frequently usurps the empire of reason.

The capacity of the stomach as well as its ability to digest is limited. The stomach is equipped for only a limited amount of food and is normally satisfied with that amount. If we give it more, the digestion becomes slow and difficult. Instead of the surplus food serving the ends of nutrition, it rather impedes them. The gastric activities quickly weaken and the superfluous food is ejected without benefit, but not without damage to the organism. It is not sufficient to eat, but that which is eaten must also be digested. Food that the stomach cannot assimilate is lost and weakens not only the digestive apparatus, but, by reaction, the whole body.

This truth, so loudly proclaimed by hygiene, cannot be too often called to the attention of those who are inclined to sacrifice their stomach to the pleasures of the palate and can never resist the temptation of a good meal.

Heavy eaters may enjoy a certain popularity, but they no longer have a good stomach, and, without any show of reason they try to convince themselves that the more one eats, the more one digests. If they are placed on a rational diet, discomfort, gastric troubles, and attacks of weakness continue, which clearly indicates the force of habit. Overeating has gradually brought about an overexcitation of the stomach, *i. e.,* a fictitious activity of which they have become the slaves and victims. It is to this overirritation that they owe their dilated stomach with all its evil effects.

The intimate relation existing between the brain and the stomach explains the violent reactions which intemperance exercises upon the system, upon the emotions, and upon reason. We shall indicate these effects briefly.

Nutrition is attacked and more or less profoundly disturbed. The digestive organs are predisposed to congestions.

The higher emotions are impaired, whilst the

lower are strengthened. The senses become dull, memory fades, the imagination is weakened, whilst the evil instincts are aroused. The *bon-vivant* is never satisfied with good food, but inevitably craves sensual pleasure.

Need we add that excesses in eating paralyze and weaken the intellect? Heavy eaters are often men of small minds. Excess in eating renders mental activity temporarily impossible. How can a person think freely and correctly, when the blood is surcharged with waste products and diverted from the brain to the digestive organs? Great geniuses are often by nature abstemious.

If the effects of gluttony are so ruinous, those of intemperate drinking are even more terrible. The former vice is all too widespread, but the latter is even more common. The abuse of intoxicating liquors has fastened itself upon all classes of society and causes the greatest havoc everywhere. Let us briefly study the effects of alcoholism.

Whenever a person drinks a quart of wine or a large glass of whiskey, he becomes *drunk*. The loss of reason, the disturbance of the brain, and the trembling of the limbs indicate this state, which lasts but a few hours. But drunkenness rarely occurs only once in a lifetime. "He who has drunk, will drink again." Acute alcoholism leads to chronic alcoholism. Whether drunkenness is produced by frequent public excesses or whether it occurs in secret and as a consequence of the regular and daily use of alcohol, the result is essentially the same.

The stomach is the first organ attacked by the poison. A chronic catarrh accompanied by vomiting makes its appearance. Digestion becomes difficult, and the appetite is lost. The liver and the kidneys are affected; all the organs are eventually damaged. The least accident may cause a premature death.

Since alcohol is a poison which attacks the most delicate tissues, it is not surprising that it should cause disturbances of the nervous system. The drunkard becomes sleepless and loses strength. His gaze is fixed and stupid. His hands tremble or suffer from cramps. The emotions deteriorate and the reasoning power becomes dulled. "Reason disappears in the depth of the glass." Nightmares and hallucinations make their appearance, and in the end paralysis, or *delirium tremens,* prostrates the unfortunate drinker.

The drunkard is afflicted not only in his own person, but also in his progeny. His virility, of course, has not vanished, but it has deteriorated. As a consequence, his children bear the imprint of his vice. If they are not cursed by an almost insuperable craving for strong alcoholic drinks, they are at least disposed to convulsions, nervous ailments, hysteria, epilepsy, idiocy, and insanity.

In view of these facts alcoholism presents itself as a degrading vice, which ruins the individual and the family, and as a "social peril," which must be resolutely combated. Unfortunately, the State receives enormous revenues from the tax on alcohol, and therefore, in regard to the suppression of drunkenness, is confronted by the serious alternative of choosing between revenue and duty.[1]

Another important source of revenue (*i. e.*, that from the sale of tobacco) would also be diminished if the people were protected against the temptations of the cabarets.[2] It has been said that "tobacco and alcohol render each other a mutual but not very honorable service." [3] The use of tobacco in excess, like that of wine, gradually undermines the nervous system. It is a passion that corresponds to no real need of our body, and therefore can never receive the approbation of hygiene. Why, then, does it find grace with moralists?

[1] The suppression of drunkenness is one thing and absolute prohibition is another. The result of prohibition in the United States shows that absolute prohibition increases the evils rather than diminishes them. If any alleviation is to be expected, it must come from a rational and religious education together with sane regulation by the State. (*Tr.*).

[2] The prohibition experiment in the United States has proved that the closing of saloons, cabarets, etc., makes no difference in the sale of tobacco.

[3] *Hygiène pour Tous*, p. 236.

# CHAPTER VII

## COMMERCIAL AND INDUSTRIAL FRAUDS

Foods must be natural, healthful, and free from every adulteration that would render them unfit for nourishment or injurious to health. This is absolutely required by hygiene and imperiously demanded by moral science. But commercial frauds have never been more frequent, more open, and more dangerous than in our day; either because scientific progress makes such adulterations easier than formerly, or because the necessary supervision on the part of the authorities has become less strict, or, finally, because the principles of religious morality are misunderstood and disregarded more than ever before. It is probable that all these causes are coöperating.

*A correct conscience condemns every concealment of an injury to an article of food, which injury is not evident, or known only to the seller, and the moralists of all times, theologians, canonists, casuists, and economists have expressed their unalterable condemnation of adulteration.*[1] *It is absolutely forbidden,*

[1] Cfr. St. Thomas, *Summa Theologica*, 2a 2æ, qu. 77, art. 2–3.

*knowingly to deceive an unsuspicious and confiding customer as to the nature of a given object as well as to its weight and price.* These are fundamental truths of the moral law of nature, which are, moreover, confirmed by the Decalogue.

Unfortunately these fundamental principles of morality, no matter how well they may be established, are hardly taught nowadays, but have succumbed to the fate of religion, and commercial frauds would stand a good chance of prospering and remaining unpunished, did they not so seriously imperil public health and were they not so severely condemned by hygiene.

All physicians know that adulterated food slowly but surely exercises a pernicious effect upon the organs of the body, and many consumers, who for a long time were indifferent or ignorant concerning this matter, are becoming disquieted. True, the public authorities are occupying themselves more and more with the disgraceful adulterations to which nearly all ordinary food products are subjected, and which gradually rob the people of strength and health, whilst they quickly fill the coffers of avaricious speculators. But the mere making of laws is not sufficient; they must also be enforced. The laws that are on the statute books are but too often inefficacious, either because the people do not invoke them, or because science is not far enough advanced to detect the frauds that are forbidden, or because the State has not enough inspectors.[2]

The adulterations practiced are so varied and numerous that they have given rise to voluminous treatises on the subject,[3] and that new monographs appear almost daily. We shall content ourselves with mentioning the most common and reprehensible adulterations, which concern the necessary foods.

The most important adulteration is that of wheat flour, from which our bread is made. Some millers add inferior or cheaper meals of other grains (maize, rice, etc.). Meal of legumes (finely ground cowpeas, soya beans, lentils, peas), nay, even potato starch, are added to rye and wheat flour, and nothing less than a chemical and microscopic analysis can detect these frauds.

Millers vie with one another to prepare a flour

[2] And in the United States we may add: or because many inspectors accept bribes and enrich themselves at the expense of the purse and health, nay, of the life, of the community. Though the morale of the corps of pure food inspectors has been improved, the evil example of the innumerable corrupt and hypocritical prohibition agents has not been without its disastrous effects upon the enforcement of the pure food laws. The greatest aid in obtaining pure food has, perhaps, been the law which forces all manufacturers to print on the label of their wares a list of the ingredients contained therein. (*Tr.*)

[3] We cite especially the *Dictionnaire des Altérations et Falsifications* by Chevallier and Baudrimont, and the *Encyclopedia Americana,* art. "Adulteration."

which is as white as possible, because even though it be of a very inferior quality, it commands a higher price, since it makes a finer bread. But unfortunately the whiteness of the flour is in inverse ratio to its nutritive value, because this whiteness is effected by extracting the glutinous or nitrogenous elements of the grain. The whiteness of the flour, moreover, favors the addition of starches. Many millers, in order to make their flour whiter, mix it with alum. This bleaches the flour and gives it a flavor resembling that of the hazelnut.[4] Baron de Coninck van Mercken some time ago reported to the Belgian Senate that there are mills in that country ·which use vast quantities of alum a year, and demanded the immediate suppression of the practice referred to.

Meat, too, is frequently tampered with. Sometimes the meat offered for sale in butcher shops has become tainted either by disease or by heat, and is good for nothing except to be destroyed. The meat of calves born dead is indigestible and dangerous and should never be sold as food.

The butchers, however, are not always to blame

[4] This taste, natural to flour, is lost in flour produced by the new milling machinery—a warning to those who bake hosts for the Holy Sacrifice of the Mass to be careful that they get genuine wheat flour from honest millers. If they cannot obtain sufficient guarantees, let them purchase flour for altar wafers from a reliable religious house, e. g., St. Mary's Mission House, Techny, Ill.

for the inferior quality of their meat. The fault often lies with the cattle-raisers, who subject cattle to a feeding process which is financially advantageous to them, but cannot be justified hygienically. Calves and hogs are quickly and cheaply fattened with slop from distilleries and beet-sugar refineries, thus furnishing meat of apparently fine quality, but actually unfit for human consumption.

A similar procedure is sometimes adopted in the production of milk. By a special feeding process speculators obtain an abundant yield of milk. The quantity is enormous, but at the expense of quality. Hygiene can never approve of such practices, which violate both nature and justice.

The adulteration of milk is very frequent, and is as criminal as the adulteration of flour, since this precious liquid is the only and necessary nourishment of little children and of many invalids. The explanation of milk adulteration is to be found in the importance of the milk-trade and lack of conscience on the part of the vendors, as well as in the great number of middlemen who participate in the profits from the moment the milk leaves the cow's udder until it is delivered to the consumer. The most usual method of adulteration consists in separating all or part of the cream from the milk and then adding more or less water.

Wine, which in many countries is an article of

daily consumption, has become the object of adulteration to such an extent that many consumers no longer know *the natural product of the vine*.[5]

The trade in brandies and whiskies demands as careful a supervision as that in wine. Since spirits of wine are rare and expensive, a cheaper grade of alcohol is used as a substitute and the resulting product is harmful and poisonous.[6]

We shall not enter into a discussion of the adulterations of beer, cider, olive oil, vinegar, butter, and other food products, because such a discussion would lead us too far afield. The practitioners of such vile swindling operations are not deterred even by the most stringent laws, because their eyes are fixed only on gain, and they find it more advantageous to pay

[5] We omit Dr. Surbled's detailed account of the methods employed in adulterating wine as of no particular value in a country where the manufacture and sale of wine are forbidden by law. Priests should be very careful in buying altar wines, especially imported. The *Encyclopedia Americana* has the following under the title "Wines" in the article "Adulteration": "Cheap foreign wines should be understood from the outset to be made either from exhausted grapeskins or raisins treated with alcohol and water (it is not for dessert use that the great bulk of the California raisin crop is exported to France) or from pear juice (much the greater part of the so-called French 'champagne' being perry)."

[6] These remarks of the author apply with even greater force to the United States. There is no supervision of the illegal product of the "moonshiner's" still, and frequently he produces downright poison. The results to public health are appalling.

an occasional fine than to uphold righteousness and honor. The laws against adulteration of foods are useful and necessary for the protection of the public health, yet they must remain ineffectual as long as the consciences of men are not enlightened and subject to the eternal law of God, which says: *Thou shalt not take thy neighbor's goods or knowingly retain them.*

# CHAPTER VIII

## THE HOUSING PROBLEM

HYGIENE and moral science agree in explaining to man his duties in the things that concern nutrition; and they also concur in tracing for him the rules which must govern his housing. Moral teaching stands on too high a plane to occupy itself with the measurements of living quarters or a thousand other details, which are very important for bodily health, yet it finds all these things in the precepts of hygiene, which insure the full development of our being, and thus moral science gives its approval to all those reform movements which combat squalor and vice.

In our large cities, where the populace pours in from all directions, and where it finds shelter only with difficulty, the question of lodging the workers is a very important one, which rightly occupies the attention of philanthropists as well as economists and scholars. As Georges Picot, who devoted his life to the study of this question, remarked, adequate housing is the "knot of the social question." [1] The loathsomeness of many of those pest-holes in which gener-

[1] *Un Devoir Social et les Logements d'Ouvrier,* 1885.

ations of unfortunate workers follow one another, accumulating vermin and dirt, surpasses all imagining. Often one room shelters a whole family or even two families. In England an official of the public health department discovered a man, a woman, four children, and three pigs living in a cellar den. In other countries unmarried laborers frequently live with their married co-laborers, and all sleep in the same room. It even happens that the same bed must serve husband, wife, children, and boarder. "Honest laborers," says Dr. Rochard, "with their families live in the midst of thieves, murderers, and prostitutes; morality and decency are unknown. Very few of these people are married, and no one cares. 'Free love' is triumphant, and frequently accompanied by incest.[2] . . . No noble sentiment can bud in such dens of vice; the family spirit vanishes. The laborer enters his dwelling with disgust, and leaves it as soon as possible, to go to some saloon, where he can forget his misery. Wife and children also go out, or pine away amidst a mixture of seduction and vice, because vice and crime flee to these infested dens and these filthy, dark alleys, where they thrive like mushrooms on a manure pile. Sloth and idleness develop

[2] That the conditions described by Balzac, de Maupassant, and Zola in France, and by Dickens and Thackeray in England, exist also in America, is evidenced by much of the American literature to-day and attested to by social workers who know the slums of our large cities. (Translator).

with them and complete the hideous circle, by which the family of the laborer is so often surrounded." [3]

This deplorable condition has for a long time attracted attention. Public opinion has stood aghast, and the authorities have sought for means of a cure. Comfortable homes for laborers, nay whole labor colonies, have been built under the best hygienic conditions in the midst of large cities, and many consider the problem of poverty solved by the erection of cheap houses. But all this amounts to naught. For as Dr. Rochard remarks: "It is an easy matter everywhere to shelter the better class of laborers. For this no intervention is necessary. The difficulty commences when there is question of the masses; and it becomes almost insurmountable when there is question of those lowest strata of society which the English call *residuum* and which M. Raffalovich designates as *the scum of poverty*. In these lowest strata we must not only furnish the families with suitable habitations, but we must also teach them how to use them, *i. e.*, instil into them the spirit of order and cleanliness, without which there can be no permanently healthy dwelling. It is far more difficult to change the habits of these unfortunates than to build houses for them."

Short-sighted philanthropists cannot understand that the demands of morality precede those of hy-

[3] *Questions d'Hygiène Sociale*, pp. 176-180.

giene and that the reform of the individual must precede that of his lodging. All the unfortunate beings who inhabit our suburbs [4] have souls, which are, *as a rule, much more neglected than their bodies,* and for this reason they live like beasts. Give them an ideal, give them a religion, enlighten their consciences, strengthen their wills and soon, with progress in morality, domestic order and economy will prevail.

Furthermore, hygienic dwellings are still too rare, and, for the generality of the poorer classes, too expensive. Therefore, we must in the first place direct our attention to the amelioration of the sanitary conditions of the quarters in which they now live. Aside from the absolute neglect of moral principles, which we have so emphatically pointed out, the opposition and indifference of the property owners forms an almost insurmountable obstacle. The reason is that the landlords draw a *large income* from these infested quarters and care more for temporal advantages than for duty.[5]

Hotels and rooming-houses are frequently the

[4] In European cities laborers live in the suburbs (faubourgs, Vorstädte) ; in America they mostly inhabit the slums. (Translator).

[5] These poorly kept and poorly repaired dwellings often yield an income of seven, eight, nay, ten per cent. (This is true also in America both for the city and the country. Renters on farms cannot even get a roof repaired, yet must render one-fourth of the crops.' (Tr.)

breeding places of moral and physical infection, and yet the State is not impotent in this matter, if it really wishes to enforce order and hygiene. Why, then, are these hotels and inns and rooming-houses not more strictly and efficiently supervised? Most of the rooms are narrow, without sufficient light and air, and inadequately partitioned off; hence, healthy life is impossible, and vice spreads easily. But what shall we say of the unhealthy as well as immoral double beds, so highly prized in these places? What shall we think of the common dormitories, where the most elementary rules of decency are outraged, especially, if both sexes congregate there? The abominations of furnished rooms are but too well known for us to point them out; yet we ask ourselves, why do not the authorities, who are assisted by the most stringent ordinances, put an end to these disorders?

True, laws cannot guide man without the aid of good morals; and for that very reason religion remains the great school of honor and morality. In spite of the senseless war, which those in power carry on against the Gospel in France and other countries, the Gospel yet remains the most effective code for the suppression of our evil inclinations and for our guidance on the path to virtue. Human society can find its salvation only in the Cross. If only the opponents of the Gospel would think of this before it is too late!

He who allows himself to be guided by the laws of morality spontaneously arrives at a point where he will observe the fundamental precepts of hygiene. If the latter regards a room in which a person can breathe easily, as necessary, the former insures bodily health by requiring a separate bed for each person, and further by imperiously demanding the separation of the sexes and ages, and by insisting on respect for innocence, modesty, and decency.

Separation of individuals is most favorable to healthy sleep. Sharing the same bed, which disturbs sleep and excites the nerves, can be justified at most in the married state, though even there it has its inconveniences. Hence married people advanced in years in the interests of their health no longer share the same bed. The rule of isolation applies especially to children, who are thereby preserved from grave dangers, especially of impurity. Not only must boys and girls be separated, but every child should have its own bed. If the number of beds is not sufficient, the separation may be effected in a large bed by letting one child sleep at the upper end of the bed and the other at the lower end; but in this case careful surveillance is necessary. The sleeping together of an adult and a child cannot be approved either from the hygienic or from the moral standpoint, though at times it may not be easy to arrange things otherwise. But children under eighteen months of age should sleep neither with the mother nor with the nurse, because of the danger of death to the child; they should lie in their cradles. All these precautionary regulations are not useless; they protect the innocence of the children. St. Francis de Sales called the attention of Madame de Chantal to them in an especial manner, when he wrote to her: "Your children must sleep alone, as much as possible, or at least with persons whom you can trust as much as yourself. You cannot imagine how useful this advice is; experience calls it to my attention daily."

Whether the children sleep alone or not, surveillance is always necessary. Up to the moment when they go to sleep in the evening, as well as when they awake in the morning, the eye of the parents exercises a moral influence upon them, by preventing and restraining the first temptation to yield to the solitary vice.

The interest of the family demands that parents and children should live together, but there arises a difficult and important question: Should the beds of the children be in the same room as that of the parents? Here we are involuntarily reminded of the old saying: *"Maxima puero debetur reverentia."* The reserve and prudence of parents, as well as the presence of curtains and other arrangements can insure the observation of decency; but do these means suffice to protect the innocence of the children?

Should they not be preserved absolutely from the always possible and always dangerous sight of conjugal caresses? It is much safer to assign to the children a bedroom away from that of the parents.

The sleeping together of adults is condemned by hygiene and especially by morality because it disturbs bodily rest and foments evil inclinations. Who can say what shameful deeds it has provoked, and how many innocent persons it has corrupted? The practice cannot be too severely condemned.

The housing of servants has also become a serious question of hygiene and morality in the mansions of the rich. Formerly the servants formed a part of the family; they were loyally subject to their masters, shared faith and morals with them, and slept in their immediate vicinity, in order to be on hand at night as well as in the daytime in case of necessity. To-day the servants form a class apart, whose service during the day is regulated in detail and paid for by the day or hour. Their employers no longer have any claim on them at night. By giving them liberty, the servants are relegated to the garret rooms, where men and maid servants live in dangerous proximity without the least supervision. Vice does not necessarily come into existence under such conditions, but it arises only too easily from the daily and forced proximity of the sexes in narrow corridors and small unhealthy bedrooms.

Sexual irregularities are the almost inevitable result of such arrangements, and promote the spread of syphilis and other venereal diseases, which, in turn, threaten the welfare of the family. By reason of the latter fact this matter, without losing its moral aspect, becomes a hygienic question of the first importance. Hence, it vitally interests even those physicians who are indifferent to the salvation of souls, yet wish to provide for the corporal welfare of those under their care. But they will never really solve the problem.

In order to protect the health and independence of the employers as well as the morals of the servants, a certain French physician, Dr. Lanteirès, suggested that two houses be built side by side and connected at each story by galleries; the employers to live in one and the servants in the other. But since this ingenious plan requires much space and expenditure, there is little hope of its being accepted by architects; and yet the existing condition of affairs, which is daily growing more serious, obliges us to seek a radical remedy. The practice of lodging the servants away from the family is unacceptable; they should rather be brought back to their true place near their masters. It seems to us that a return to the old traditions is absolutely necessary, and that a loyal and Christian servant class, treated with justice and kindness, will not only insure satisfactory service, but also help to bridge over, to some extent at least, the yawning abyss which exists to-day between the various classes of society. The master would show more solicitude and the servants greater obedience, and all, being true Christians, would never forget that they are brethren in the Lord.

# CHAPTER IX

HYGIENE teaches and proves the utility of clothing. Clothes preserve the natural warmth of the body, protect it against accidents and changes of weather, and promote the secretive functions of the skin. But is clothing always and everywhere indispensable? Is it absolutely necessary? Can its necessity be proved in the same experimental manner as its utility? Science could not assert this necessity without meeting contradiction.

No one denies the importance of clothing in the temperate zone and especially in the cold regions of the North. But it diminishes as we go south, and vanishes beneath the glowing sun of the tropics. It is here that the needs of the soul make themselves felt besides those of the body, and the question transcends the narrow limits of hygiene.

Clothing is not merely a physical necessity, it is also and especially a moral necessity. Be it ever so scant, it covers nakedness, safeguards innocence, and protects modesty.

Conscience urges us to wear clothing; and we

could not correctly understand this strict servitude
if we did not know that it is a deserved punishment
entailed by original sin. Adam and Eve in Paradise
enjoyed a superabundant life, free from our weaknesses and frailties. "They were both naked," says
Sacred Scripture, "and were not ashamed." (Gen.
II, 25.)

When their disobedience, overthrowing the designs of Providence, had led them out into a world
filled with sorrows, they were ashamed in each other's presence and immediately felt the need of clothing. Shame, then, appeared simultaneously with labor and disease, and all three are evident signs
of sin and degradation. All nations, even the most
savage and inferior, know the emotion of shame.
It is a truly human emotion, which would be inexplicable without the doctrine of original sin. We
find it in some idiots, and our materialists believe
they have discovered it in their cousins, the anthro-
poid apes.

Now, even though shame exists in every one of
us, it is far from being invulnerable; on the contrary, it is quite fragile. It is, moreover, constantly
exposed to the attacks of the evil passions, and
must, therefore, be carefully nurtured and protected. Furthermore, it arrives at its full development only at the age of puberty; and until that
time it is the duty of parents to safeguard it

in their children. The manner in which children are dressed should be in accord with this principle. Shame has the precedence over the duties of health, and furthermore, adapts itself admirably to the rules of hygiene.

We will here call attention to the usefulness of drawers or "bloomers" for little girls. This garment is frequently left off, either for reasons of economy or because of the heat in summer. But it has indisputable hygienic value and it protects the child from touches, excitations, and dangerous occasions.

For the same and even more urgent reasons young girls and women should not discard this useful article of clothing, even though it seems sometimes rather inconvenient. It protects them from severe colds, conforms to the most elementary decency, and protects that most beautiful of virtues, modesty.

Unfortunately, modern fashions are prone to disregard the principles of morality as well as of hygiene, and to pervert morals. Whilst women of the proletariat leave off their drawers without a thought, society ladies discard an essential part of dress and boldly expose their breasts and backs to the gaze of the public at balls and soirées. This *décolletage* in its various degrees—and we cannot always say where it will stop—is as indecent as it is unhealthy. It causes numerous diseases of the respiratory organs.

The breasts are delicate and susceptible organs of the female anatomy and to expose them violates the laws of hygiene as well as those of morality. Therefore these *society customs* must be absolutely condemned. Let the married woman keep her "charms" for her husband, and let the young maiden religiously preserve them for him who is to have the honor of founding a family with her.

But, unfortunately, the woman who wishes to seduce and to please by no means contents herself with exhibiting her natural charms; she strives to intensify them and to beautify herself by artificial means. False hair, paint, powder, and perfume reveal the coquetry of woman, but also prove, on the other hand, her strange disregard for hygiene. These frequently dangerous aids to beauty offend no less against nature than against good taste, and can certainly not be considered strictly moral.

The eccentricities of fashion, by which woman permits herself to be led, and which often serve her as an excuse, make her misconceive the most fundamental laws of the human body. The corset, for example, answers no need of the body, and causes the most deplorable disorders.[1]

In order to comply with the laws of hygiene, and to protect her honor and virtue, woman need but

[1] Happily most American women have discarded this instrument of torture. (Tr.)

rely on the charms with which Providence has blessed her. By exhibiting them simply and modestly, she can secure the respect of man and preserve her self-esteem. The recent attempts to force male attire upon women are ridiculous. Man and woman were ordained to complement each other in marriage; but by nature they are different, and the difference of their functions justifies a difference of attire. This fact suffices, and we need not enter into the reasons of propriety and decency which demand this difference.

# CHAPTER X

## EXERCISE AND LABOR

CONSIDERED relatively, and prescinding from organic and intellectual life, man is an animal destined to move. His body is a complicated assembly of bone levers, which are set in motion by muscles. Muscular exercise, far from being a matter of indifference to the general health, is necessary for it. Life could not be conceived without motion; *vita in motu,* said the ancients. This activity, demanded by nature, is indispensable for the satisfaction of all our needs; and physiology rightly regards it as the basis of existence.

The more we consider the hierarchy of our faculties, the more clearly do we perceive the law of action, the necessity of exercise and work. The muscle obeys the nerve; and it is the spinal and cerebral nerve centers that preside over our external activity. We know, furthermore, that the nerves are always functioning, and that they serve a thousand forms of psychic activity.

Accordingly every man is subject to the law of labor by reason of his physical constitution. This truth, which is demonstrable by science, has at all times asserted itself to the sages of the earth. *"Man,"* says Job (V, 7), *"is born to labor as the bird is born to fly."* This inevitable law, imposed by the exigencies of daily life, is a hard law, which we obey only because we must, at times with sighs and not without utmost fatigue and bitter sweat. We cannot explain its rigor nor comprehend its justice except in the light of Christian faith.

We must all, in our fallen nature, submit to that punishment which was pronounced upon sinful Adam. *"In the sweat of thy brow thou shalt eat thy bread,"* (Gen. III, 19) said the Lord to our guilty progenitor, and labor, which was always a law, became thenceforth a painful and depressing duty, the mark of original sin.

However, labor, as we must perform it, offers superabundant compensations for our pains. Without speaking here of the atonement which faith discovers in it, and the merits which can be gained by labor, we will only point out that manual labor is the surest guarantee of physical health.

Muscular exercise, especially when it is regular and methodical, expends nervous energy in a useful manner, stimulates circulation, respiration, and excretion, promotes nutrition, and contributes not only to the maintenance of functional harmony, but also to firmness of character as well as to the prevention of diseases and infirmities.

The exercise of the spiritual faculties, whether in a practical form (*e. g.,* by manufacturers, merchants, etc.) or in a speculative form (*e. g.,* by theologians, philosophers, scholars, etc.) is more fatiguing and requires more caution than purely muscular activity. It must be combined with the former in exact proportions, in order to counterbalance psychic labor with external activity. Walks, gymnastics, horseback riding, gardening, and all other muscular exercises are to be recommended to mental workers as means of distraction.

Hence labor is a law for all mankind. Whether the hand, armed with a spade, digs a ditch, or the mind seeks to discover the laws of attraction, our nature does not know continued repose; it must be always occupied. Inaction is physiologically an impossibility; it is the contradiction of life itself and the sign of death. Labor shows its higher significance by providing a useful nourishment for nervous activity.

An unoccupied mind is the plaything of the imagination, the prey of the passions, the slave of low impulses. Idleness, by suppressing regular exercise of the muscles, not only destroys the vitality of the body, but also attacks the will and quickly destroys the energy of even the most courageous soul. Idleness is the great enemy of man and, as has been rightly said, "the beginning of all vice." It seems tainted by a Satanic malice, since it seeks to annul the law of labor imposed by God Himself.

Thus labor in its various forms is the great and only remedy. It serves not only the important interests of hygiene, but also forms the solid basis of a truly moral life. It preserves body and soul from inevitable collapse. By reason of its salutary influence, the soul no longer experiences ennui, that evil counselor, and no longer remains subject to the disgraceful slavery of sensual desires, but gains possession of itself and of nature.

Labor also has its special joys and benefits. It assures our well-being by satisfying our needs and meeting our desires, and aids in developing those thousands of resources whose sum total constitutes the crown of civilization. But all these advantages, of which political economy boasts, and which daily seduce so many hearts, would not be able to inure us permanently to labor, and could not make us forget, or at least joyfully bear, this heavy yoke, did we not know that this yoke was once borne and ennobled, and offered to us for our magnanimous acceptance by the God-man. Who would not follow in the footsteps of the Divine Laborer? Should we not love labor, since Jesus, the Son of God, did not disdain it? [1]

[1] On labor as a natural duty, a religious necessity, and a moral obligation, see Koch-Preuss, *A Handbook of Moral Theology*. St. Louis, Herder, Vol. III, pp. 125 ff.—(Tr.)

# CHAPTER XI

THE law of labor is universal and necessary. How must it be applied in the various professions? What, especially, are the conditions under which the ordinary laborer should work? These are the subject of this important chapter. We shall follow in our exposition the precepts of an incomparable teacher, Pope Leo XIII, who, in his Encyclical *Rerum Novarum* has so admirably laid down the principles governing the social question.

Intellectual labor need not long detain us. When it is relied upon to provide the necessities of life, it is usually subject to the rigorous demands of a master in public or private offices, and we know that office employees as a rule are oppressed neither by the amount of their labor, nor by the number of hours they must work.[1] Their regular but monot-

---

[1] This can hardly be said of the private concerns in money-mad America. Many office workers work harder and longer hours than the manual laborers. They are paid more than in France, but not in proportion to the work they perform. —(Translator).

onous existence is agreeable enough, but poorly paid.

The manual labor of the ordinary workingman arrests the attention of hygienists and moralists because it has given rise to terrible abuses. Where labor is unorganized, the employers are absolutely free in their choice of laborers, who present themselves in great numbers as so many hungry beggars. As a consequence they are frequently underpaid and overworked. Unrestrained competition leads to the employment of women and children, who naturally work for lower wages than the men, because they would like to supply the most urgent needs of the household. The laborers are at times cunningly solicited and at times dismissed without a word of explanation, according to the number of orders received, and therefore, have no secure means of livelihood. Their labor is poorly paid, and they are in a constant state of worry, with no assurance for the future. Such a state of affairs entails disregard of the essential laws of hygiene and morality. The results are deplorable. The body is forced to overexert itself and quickly tires, and the soul, which has been enslaved in a similar manner, loses the consciousness of its higher destiny, and is submerged in a brutish existence.[2]

[2] In recent years mental labor, in as far as it must serve to gain a livelihood, has approached manual labor more and more in its demands upon human strength. It was hardly to be expected that, in the reconstruction of the various coun-

Pope Leo XIII strikingly dealt with the manifold aspects of this great question in his Encyclical, and his teaching is summarized in the following passage: "If we turn now to the things exterior and corporeal, the first concern of the State is to save the poor workers from the cruelty of grasping speculators, who use human beings as mere instruments for making money. It is neither justice nor humanity so to grind men down with excessive labor as to stupefy their minds and wear out their bodies. Man's powers, like his general nature, are limited, and beyond these limits he cannot go. His strength is developed and increased by use and exercise, but only on condition of due intermission and proper rest. Daily labor, therefore, must be so regulated that it may not be protracted longer than strength admits. How many and how long the intervals of rest should be, will depend upon the nature of the work, on circumstances of time and place, and on the health and strength of the workman. Those who labor in mines and quarries, and work within the bowels of the earth, should have shorter hours in proportion as their labor is more severe and more trying to the health. Then again, the season of the year must be taken into account; for not infre-

tries following the World War, mental labor should experience any alleviation; the demise of so many mental laborers excluded this. (Dr. Sleumer).

quently a kind of labor is easy at one time which at another is intolerable or very difficult.

"Finally, work which is suitable for a strong man cannot reasonably be required from a woman or a child. And in regard to children, great care should be taken not to place them in workshops and factories until their bodies and minds are sufficiently mature. For just as rough weather destroys the buds of spring, so a too early experience of life's hard work blights the young promise of a child's powers and makes any real education impossible. Women, again, are not suited to certain trades; for a woman is by nature fitted for home work, and it is that which is best adapted at once to preserve her modesty and to promote the proper bringing up of children and the well-being of the family." [3]

This masterly page from Leo XIII's encyclical letter is more thorough than a voluminous treatise and it brings out the various points in question in a convincing manner. On the one hand, he stresses the importance of taking into account age, sex, and hours of work, on the other hand, he demonstrates that these three fundamental points have the closest connection with the kind of labor performed. We, also, shall follow this natural as well as logical division and sketch the requirements of hygiene and morality in general outline.

[3] *Rights of Capital and Labor,* by Pope Leo XIII (Catholic Truth Society).

The duration of manual labor depends upon conditions which are too changeable to be uniformly and absolutely pre-determined. No state law could determine the number of hours which every individual laborer should work without violating justice, health, and logic. It is not the least of the errors of modern Socialism that it did not realize this truth when it drafted its demand of *three eights, i. e.,* eight hours for work, eight hours for sleep, and eight hours for meals and recreation. The hours of labor must necessarily stand in proper relation to the expenditure of strength which it requires, and we know how extraordinarily the latter varies in various occupations. The forms of labor differ to such an extent that it is impossible to require the same number of hours of all laborers. No one will ever admit an equality between him who has an easy and agreeable occupation and another whose task is hard and laborious. The labor of the artist cannot be compared to that of a miner, nor can that of a printer be compared to that of a farmer. Between the one and the other the duration of labor may vary as much as one-third, according to the difficulty of the work. Hence the working day may vary from eight to twelve hours; but can hardly exceed this latter limit without danger to the laborer. According to the seasons a further difference of two hours can be taken into account. In many vocations persons work without difficulty from ten to eleven hours in summer, whilst in winter eight to nine hours of the same work must suffice. Finally, the ability to work overtime and, therefore, the possibility of useful and possible labor, varies extraordinarily according to race, climate, and temperament.

Age must also be taken into consideration. Men advanced in years cannot cope with young men in the full vigor of life, and the same amount of work cannot be exacted from youths as from adults, from children as from persons in the prime of life. Youth has a right to special protection, and the employment of children under thirteen years of age in factories and workshops should be forbidden. Even until eighteen the young man's strength should be husbanded and he should not be compelled to do excessive labor or labor unsuited to his age.

Woman is destined by nature for domestic work, but frequently necessity forces her to earn her bread by hard labor outside the home. Here, too, it is the State's duty to intervene and to determine by law the exact amount and kind of work she may perform. Woman must, as far as possible, be spared hard labor. Especially must she enjoy an ample and effective protection when she is about to become a mother. In the year 1890 the International Congress at Berlin decided with sound common sense that the acceptance of any work outside the home should be forbidden by law to all mothers during the first four weeks after childbirth.

It is not, however, sufficient to give the laborer work suitable to his physical strength; he must also be protected against accidents. The law may provide the necessary protection either with or without the coöperation of the employers. Occupations which are in themselves hazardous require numerous regulations calculated to prevent injury to the workers. Are these regulations always conscientiously followed in practice? Do the federal and state inspectors take their duties seriously? Is the health of millers, for example, properly protected in the hermetically sealed rooms in which they are compelled to breathe an unhealthy mixture of dust and air for many long hours? [4]

Finally, there are dangerous branches of industry. Are the necessary and indispensable precautions to protect the life and health of the laborers always taken? Does the state always fulfill its duty of surveillance? Unfortunately, recent facts show that the public authorities as well as the managers of industries do not always take sufficient care of the workmen. The manner of conducting mines, in which numberless people daily expose their lives to danger, does not as yet conform to the laws of physiology

[4] Modern mechanical devices have greatly diminished this evil.

nor to the most necessary requirements of hygiene.
The horrible accidents that occur ever so often excite public opinion and cause investigations, but seldom lead to any radical reform.[5] Miners are accused of imprudence or negligence, but what about
the responsibility of the engineers and employers?

Most shops and factories are to-day equipped with
engines or electric motors which drive the machinery.
But the belts which transmit power are open and
easily accessible, and frequently occasion deplorable accidents. Prudent employers cover these belts
carefully with wooden or metal casings. Why is
not this practice general, and why is it not made
obligatory by law?[6] When the belts of a machine
are about to come off, no laborer should touch them
until the machine has come to a stop. This wise precaution is not always observed, and few employers
consider it a duty to restrain an overzealous workman; most of them tolerate or even encourage
the infraction of this ordinance. Loss of time is
thus avoided, but accidents are invited. An hour is
perhaps gained, but a human life may be lost or some-

[5] At Courrières, France, some years ago 1500 miners lost
their lives, partly because of the lack of rescuing apparatus,
such as gas masks, ladders, etc. (Dr. Sleumer).

[6] In all large factories in the United States this requirement is fairly well complied with, but there are still many
small factories, saw-mills, etc., that do not comply with the
law. Why not? (Translator).

one may become a cripple.[7] Can an honest conscience
hesitate in the face of such an alternative?

[7] The demands made on behalf of laborers are met in
Germany by the Social Legislation of 1890 as well as by the
workers' coöperatives. Industrial child labor is almost entirely abolished; and for female and youthful laborers there
are extensive labor limitations. Industrial inspection provides
for the observance of the legal regulations in regard to the
time of labor (night work), safeguards, dressing and rest
rooms. Through the labor unions the wages and the hours
of work are regulated by a tariff. In cases of disability, the legal
sick, accident, invalid, and old age insurance steps in. (Dr.
Sleumer). We in America are not quite so fortunate. Though
the labor unions have to a great extent alleviated the lot
of the laborer, great abuses still exist. In 1900, 120,602 women
were working in cotton mills alone, over 20% being married. In 1924 Goodsell wrote: "Since 1870, the census returns
show a large increase in child labor in this country, and a
greater range of industries in which children are employed."
(*Eccl. Rev.*, Feb. 1927, p. 117.) (Tr.)

# CHAPTER XII

## REST

WHATEVER form labor may take, it requires *rest* as its natural corollary. Everyone who works must replenish his strength and rest in proportion to the expenditure made by the organism. This is a necessity of nature. The amount of rest required depends upon the kind of work done and upon the sex, constitution, and age of the laborer. Hence this question is extremely intricate, and in order to simplify it we shall consider here the case of an adult of ordinary strength.

In general, we may say that work and rest should divide the day of twenty-four hours equally between themselves. Some can work twelve hours, if they work soberly, conscientiously, and without haste and waste of time; but no one works uninterruptedly, as the time for meals will interrupt his activity. The time for rest will then be applied to sleep, to eating, to recreation, and to family life. Constant work for twelve hours, however, can be endured only for six days a week, and the twelve-hour day is not practicable without the concession of a full day of rest, namely, the seventh day or Sunday. Without this concession the twelve-hour day would be impossible. Leo XIII in his admirable Encyclical points this out: "In all agreements between masters and workpeople, there is always the condition, expressed or understood, that there be allowed proper rest for soul and body. . . . The right to rest every day as well as cessation from work on the day of the Lord, must be an express or a tacit condition of every contract between employer and employee."

A twelve-hour day, moreover, is possible only during the summer season with its long days, whilst winter scarcely permits a ten-hour activity and leaves more time for rest because of the long evenings. Rest must be proportionate to the nature of the labor performed, and, as we have explained in the preceding chapter, the hours of labor must be less, the harder the task imposed. The miner, whose conditions of labor are especially hard, who works where never a ray of sunshine penetrates and never a breath of fresh air arrives, and where heat as well as fatigue oppresses him, certainly could not be held to a twelve-hour day, as could, for instance, painters and carpenters, who perform their work in the open air, amid song and conversation. After an eight or at the most ten-hour sojourn in the bowels of the earth, the miner has urgent need of returning to the fresh air, and a perfect right to refresh himself, body and soul, with a well-deserved rest.

Whether the work-day lasts eight, ten or twelve hours, in no case is the expenditure of strength equalized by sleep alone, and such work could not continue for months or years without causing a visible deterioration of the organism and a dulling of the spiritual faculties. Manual labor, to which the poor are forced by the hard and cruel demands of daily life, must be frequently interrupted by days of leisure, during which the body can relax and the soul regain possession of itself by escaping from the oppression of material things. This is a requirement of hygiene and also a moral precept; and both find their sanction in the third of the Ten Commandments, which designates every seventh day as the Lord's day. (*"Remember that thou keep holy the Sabbath day!"*)

The necessity of *Sunday rest* is based upon the laws of physiology, confirmed by experience. Whilst the necessity of this law for a short time was not duly recognized in consequence of the prevalence of revolutionary views, it has, nevertheless, in course of time manifested itself so clearly that many countries have established Sunday rest by law.

The Sunday rest must be observed not only because it is necessary for the corporal welfare of the laboring classes, but especially because it is the will of God and because it provides an opportunity for the soul to render to the Creator the honor that is His due. Pope Leo XIII beautifully expresses this idea in the above-quoted Encyclical: "Life on earth, however good and desirable in itself, is not the final purpose for which man is created; it is only the way and the means to that attainment of truth and that practice of goodness in which the full life of the soul consists. It is the soul which is made after the image and likeness of God; it is in the soul that the sovereignty resides by virtue of which man is commanded to rule the creatures below him, and to use all the earth and the ocean for his profit and advantage. *'Fill the earth and subdue it; and rule over the fishes of the sea, and the fowls of the air, and all living creatures which move upon the earth'.* (Gen. I, 28).

"In this respect all men are equal; there is no difference between rich and poor, master and servant, ruler and ruled, *'for the same is Lord over all.'* (Rom. X, 12). No man may outrage with impunity that human dignity which God Himself treats with reverence, nor stand in the way of that higher life which is the preparation for the eternal life of Heaven. Nay, more: a man has here no power over himself. To consent to any treatment which is calculated to defeat the end and purpose of his being is beyond his right; he cannot give up his soul to servitude, for it is not man's own rights which are in question here, but the most sacred and inviolable rights of God. From this follows the obligation of the cessation of work and labor on Sundays and certain festivals. This rest from labor is not to be understood as mere idleness; much less must it be an occasion of spending money and indulging in vicious excess, as many would desire it to be; but it should ·be rest from labor consecrated to religion. Repose united with religious observance disposes man to forget for a while the business of this daily life and turn his thoughts to heavenly things and to the worship which he so strictly owes to the Eternal Deity. It is this, above all, which is the reason and the motive of the Sunday rest; a rest sanctioned by God's great law of the ancient covenant, *Remember thou keep holy the Sabbath day* (Exod. XX, 8) and taught to the world by His own mysterious 'rest' after the creation of man: *He rested on the seventh day from the work which He had done* (Gen. II, 2)."

# CHAPTER XIII

To live long, to live forever, is man's aim and fondest dream. The centenarian is regarded with curiosity and envy, even when he is subject to manifold miseries. Why? Because human existence rarely attains this span. Life so rarely exceeds a hundred years that the extension of a lifetime beyond a hundred and two, as was the lot of the renowned chemist Chevreul, was considered marvelous, by the masses as well as by himself.

*Longevity,* then, is as rare as it is proportionately short. It depends upon various conditions and especially upon the constitution of the individual. Heredity plays an important part. There are whole families of centenarians and many families in which the span of life of the individual member is generally from eighty to ninety years. In contrast to this there are other families whose members all die young. In the Turgot family no one ever reached the age of sixty, and the famous political economist of that name had a premonition of his early demise as soon as he reached his fiftieth year. Although he felt strong and healthy, he stoically prepared himself for death and actually died in his fifty-third year. The causes which, aside from heredity, determine the length or brevity of life, are as numerous as they are obscure.

Statistics is for many the science of sciences, and they look to it to reveal the secret of longevity. A German scholar named Caspar,[1] has with great patience determined the number per 100 of persons in certain professions, who attain the seventieth year. We quote his table, less for its value than for its oddity:

*Proportion*
*per 100*

*Profession*

| Theologians | 42 |
| Farmers | 40 |
| Merchants | 35 |
| Soldiers | 32 |
| Officials | 32 |
| Lawyers | 29 |
| Artists | 28 |
| Professors | 27 |
| Physicians | 24 |

[1] Johann Ludwig Caspar (1796–1861) was for many years professor at the University of Berlin. He edited two volumes, *Beiträge zur medizinischen Statistik und Staatsarzneikunde* (Berlin, 1825 and 1835), which represent the first attempt at medical statistics.

Everyone is surprised at the antithesis in this table between theologians and physicians, and it is attributed to various causes. The longevity of the former is explained by their peaceful and regular life, as well as by their good morals. The mortality of the latter has its cause in their irregular life and the dangers of their laborious profession. But aside from these reasons, which after all are but probabilities, other questions arise, to which the theory of Caspar gives us no answer, and which can never be answered by statistics alone.

Even though the true conditions of longevity are still unknown, we know definitely that excesses of every kind shorten the span of life. Intemperance is one of the most active causes of a premature death. The ancients said in perfect truth, *"Plures occidit gula quam gladius,"* i. e., more men are killed by gluttony than by the sword. But intemperance is not alone in dragging its victims to the grave; it is more easily noticed, because it is the most visible and most noisy of the passions. As a matter of fact, every passion that subjugates the human heart and is not regulated by reason, is injurious and murderous. This is especially the case with that shameful and solitary vice which prematurely exhausts the vitality of youth. A wise man has aptly said that life is given to us to be of long duration, and that we ourselves shorten it by our imprudent excesses.

From what has been said it necessarily follows that the secret of longevity is to be found, if not entirely, at least in part, in temperance as well as the observance of the laws of hygiene. *"Qui abstinens est adiiciet vitam,"* says the Book of Ecclesiastes. The story of the famous Venetian, Cornaro, is well known. He had aged prematurely as a result of his excesses, and when he was thirty years old, his bodily strength was almost gone. He then determined to lead a simple and regular life, and in this regime found the charm by which he recovered perfectly from all the ills caused by his excesses, and lived to be a contented centenarian (d. 1556). How many of us do not resist the allurements of the senses, but plunge blindly into vice and death! Temperance is, moreover, not only a duty prescribed by science; it is also a moral virtue, which serves as a basis for other virtues.[2]

The unrestrained passions are just as much the enemies of the body as they are of the soul; they must be energetically subdued and mastered. The will must regulate them and invincibly bend them to duty, which always prefers virtue to pleasure. Excesses at table are victoriously overcome by temperance; envious and angry ebullitions by meekness and mildness; impurity by chastity. In this manner we preserve peace of mind and secure the quiet and

[2] Cfr. Surbled, *Hygiène pour Tous,* pp. 223 sqq.

untrammeled development of life. If the passions are subdued, if the spirit is in a state of peace, if nervous activity experiences no vain and unregulated movements, then life flows on without let or hindrance to a beautiful old age.

But even if this terrestrial life should end a little sooner, we lose nothing by listening to hygiene and moral science and by obeying the precepts of our faith. Life—let us be sure—is the prize of virtue, the reward of a career, no matter how short, which was consecrated to God and to duty. And the heavenly life is not to be compared to this changeable and uncertain existence here on earth, which is so full of pain and sorrow. It is rather life in its fullness, superabundant, immortal life in the bosom of God, where Jesus Christ awaits us—He who has given us His Blood and His Law, who guides and supports us in our struggles here below, and who has promised to acknowledge His faithful servants as His own on the last day and to admit them to the ineffable vision of His Father, which is life everlasting.

# PART III
# DISEASE

# CHAPTER I

## SOUL AND BODY IN SICKNESS

THE unity of the human personality, so distinctly recognizable in the common or interrelational life, when all the functions are properly balanced and exercised with ease and harmony, becomes even more evident when illness upsets the system and reacts painfully on the soul by afflicting the body. There exists between these two constituent parts of our being such an intimate union and correlation that the disorders of the one almost inevitably react upon the other.

The priest and the physician are called to the bedside of the patient; and it would be a misconception of their professional duty to consider them as strangers, indifferent to one another, and to call the former "physician of the soul" and the latter "physician of the body." This would be to misunderstand the fundamental unity of our being. The priest *is* the physician of the soul, but his moral activity has a decided influence also upon the body of the patient, and to him is due the credit of many a cure that medicine could never have effected. Without dwelling on the surprising effects of the Sacraments, the

presence of the priest, the solace offered by the consolations of religion and the manifestation of conscience, often work miracles. Certain nervous afflictions are cured more quickly by frequent confession
than by drugs. But it is not so much in the cure of
disease as in its prevention that the priest achieves
his most brilliant success: his counsels supply the
patient with a true hygiene and rule of life.
Nearly all the evils that afflict us spring from neglect
of the moral law; and, as Sacred Scripture says, sickness originates in sin. Hence the priest promotes the
interests of the body by occupying himself with the
soul and is truly the physician of the entire man.

But is not this latter title applicable also to the
doctor? Is it not doing him an injustice to restrict
his solicitude to the body alone? Does medical attention consist in taking care only of the bodily
organism without regard to the soul which animates it? No practitioner who is worthy of the
name would be content with the rôle of a veterinary;
and yet the world dares to regard us as such, no
doubt to break our pride.[1]

[1] Modern materialistic medicine regards the soul as material and usurps the place of the priest, with its psychoanalysis,
"Freudian clinics," etc. The popularity of these methods shows
the subconscious yearning of the non-Catholic world for
spiritual guidance. Psychoanalysis has its proper sphere, but
it cannot supplant the Sacraments instituted by Jesus Christ,
or the guidance of a priest trained in the spiritual life. (Translator).

The materialism which so unfortunately reigns in our schools contributes not a little to the degradation and defamation of the medical profession. The physician who does not believe in a soul, or who does not recognize its sovereign influence upon life, is never more than an inadequate practitioner; he sees the evil, but does not comprehend it; he can analyze its effects, but he does not understand either its origin or its purpose. With his halting therapeutics, entirely symptomatic and superficial, he will not be able to diagnose the evil and to vanquish it.

The true physician honors himself by believing in the existence of a soul with puissant energies; he does not neglect that soul in treating the body. His consultations lead him into the domain of conscience, into the very depths of the emotional and moral life of his patient, and his directions, aimed at the restoration of physical health, must necessarily conform to the law of God.

The priest and the physician at the sickbed therefore have distinctly parallel tasks, which, however, do not antagonize each other. They both strive to restore health, but in different ways. The priest addresses himself to the soul, elevates it to God, detaches it from its base appetites, and makes it appreciate hygiene and virtue. The physician corroborates the admonitions of the priest and searches for the visible symptoms, but, being firmly convinced

of the living unity of man and of the great rôle
played by the passions, he searches also for the
invisible disorders, and frequently exhorts the soul
to use the means of sustaining the battle against disease and finally triumphing over it. The physician
who would systematically neglect the moral aspect
of the evils that afflict humanity, would be of no
more use to our bodies than the priest who paid no
attention to the close ties which bind together the
spirit and the flesh, would be to our souls.

The physical and the moral are joined together
and interpenetrate each other in man. Is it necessary
to call attention to the influence exercised by the
body upon the soul? Does not this fact appear clearly
at every moment of our existence? And is not
the evident subjection of our proud intellect calculated to make us feel our weakness and to search
our hearts? "The intellect is at the mercy of a head-
ache. The least malady renders us weak, without
strength and without thought. The faculty of think-
ing is truly and terribly dependent upon the body;
at the least shock it may be paralyzed, disordered,
or even suppressed."

The action of the soul upon the body is striking
and manifests itself by a thousand different traits.
A violent sorrow, a vivid and sudden emotion, can
upset the system, cause (it has been said) an almost
instantaneous whitening of the hair, syncope, nay,

even death in those affected with grave heart lesions. Intense joy can produce the same effect. The passions, when not regulated by reason, react upon the system and disturb the functions, so that we can justly say that "the life of the man of the world is but a slow suicide." And even physiognomy is so intimately connected with the depths of our being that it frequently betrays the state of the soul.

Although soul and body are closely united in man, they are not blended; they are not even absolutely dependent upon each other. This distinction, which belongs to our very nature and explains the contradictions of human life, cannot be sufficiently emphasized. The soul may be disquieted, tormented, and sick in a calm and active body. On the other hand, a most exalted and brilliant spirit, endowed with a firm will, may dwell in a weak and debilitated body. The immortal Pascal passed not a day without pain, and his life was short and filled with sickness. How many commanders like Turenne manifest unshaken valor in a "trembling carcass"? But, though nature offers such contrasts, we must be on our guard against seeing in these things a general rule and saying that the law of compensation presides over the union of body and soul. It is not true that a great soul always dwells in a sickly body or that a beautiful body always houses a feeble intelligence.

The soul possesses great power, in no manner dependent upon the strength of the body, which can obtain most excellent service even from an infirm instrument. The physical life becomes stronger as the moral life develops. The will, especially by the aid of religion, acquires a surprising energy, which communicates itself to the body and renders it capable of resisting the most serious accidents, nay, even death itself. History is full of such examples; we shall cite only that of the Breton peasant who, as the result of an accident, lost three limbs, which were amputated by Dr. Léseleuc of Brest, who justly attributed the success of the operation mainly to the admirable resignation of the patient. All practitioners know by experience the great importance of moral hygiene in the treatment of the sick, and the futility of the best care, when courage is lost and the will to recover is absent.[2] Professor Farabœuf used to recommend physicians "to direct into the heart of the wounded the full stream of the balm of hope." This counsel is excellent and worthy

[2] The conduct of some Protestant ministers runs contrary to the laws of therapy. They enter the room, excite the patient by harrowing descriptions of hell, sing and make a noise sufficient to kill the patient. They know nothing of the state of his soul, since he has not confessed to them, and their counterfeit consolations do harm rather than good. For this reason priests sometimes find it difficult to obtain entrance to the sick in Protestant hospitals. As a rule, however, one visit is sufficient to allay the fears of doctors and nurses.

of this noble Protestant teacher; but what enduring
and profound confidence can be instilled into those
who believe neither in God nor in a soul, and "who
are without hope"?

Faith surpasses all the vain assurances of the
world; it lives by God and for eternity. This is the
best and only sure source of comfort, the one which
gives an unalterable peace to the soul and grace
to suffer the most excruciating torments, not only
without complaint, but even with radiant joy. Happy
the man who has nourished his heart with faith in
the days of his health and whom it consoles amidst
the rude assaults of illness! At the bedside of such
a man, priest and physician experience the satisfaction of their ministrations and can coöperate by
effectively uniting their efforts for the restoration
of the body and the triumph of life over disease.

# CHAPTER II

## DUTIES OF THE SICK

THE sick have rights, derived from moral and religious laws, which the physician as well as those about them must respect, and which are rarely violated because the weakness and suffering of the patient excite pity and sympathy. But the sick also have duties, which they are frequently tempted to misunderstand or forget, and which must be constantly recalled to their attention.

The first of these duties is a filial abandonment of oneself to Divine Providence; the second is confidence in the physician and obedience to his prescriptions. These two duties really are but one; for what is the physician but the humble instrument of God and the dispenser of His benefits? The Most High Himself has blessed the ministrations of the physician and has commanded all men to honor him and to submit to him in the well-known text of Ecclesiasticus: "Honor thy physician for the need thou hast of him; for the Most High has created him. For all healing is from God and he shall receive gifts of the king. The skill of the physician shall lift up his head, and in the sight of great men he shall be praised. . . . Give sweet savor, and a memorial of fine flour, and make a fat offering, and then give place to the physician. For the Lord created him; and let him not depart from thee, for his works are necessary. For there is a time when thou must fall into their hands: And they shall beseech the Lord, that he would prosper what they give for ease and remedy, for their conversation." (Ecclus. XXXVII, 1–3; 11–14.)

Sacred Scripture admirably delineates the rôle of the physician and that of the sick man in regard to the Creator. The patient promptly resigns himself into the hands of God, and then calls in the physician. The latter is but an agent of Divine Omnipotence; he does not cure the sick, but God cures them through the physician.

It is said of St. Jean-Baptiste Vianney, the Curé of Ars, that, in a serious illness of 1843, he read the book of Ecclesiasticus, and, being penetrated by the admonitions of God, no longer hesitated to surrender himself to the physicians and to obey their directions. To how many patients, even Christian patients, could we not profitably recommend the reading of the Sacred Books and above all the sage conduct of the saintly Curé d'Ars?

The physician by no means demands of his patient a blind, instinctive obedience, but rather the *reason-*

*able obedience* mentioned by St. Paul;[1] and the Abbé Perreyve, who recommends this obedience as the honor of a Christian life, justly opposes it to "that unreasonable, senseless, unjust obedience which the patient renders to the physician contrary to duty and to conscience." This saintly priest, whom a malady of long duration acquainted so well with the duties of the sick, in an admirable passage brands *medical superstition* as a blind confidence which persuades us to expect of a man more than he can give. An inevitable consequence is a certain fanatical obedience, the effect of which is unreservedly to deliver a Christian soul to a man who, perhaps, cares nothing for the voice of God, or of conscience, or of common sense. The danger of such an excess is easily perceived. Many patients fall into the pitiful extreme of saying: "The doctor said it"; for only too many weak souls this is the supreme law; and if God Himself should contradict the physician, the patient would obey the latter. What will be the consequence if the physician, instead of being a wise, honest, enlightened, and God-fearing man, who respects the soul (whose character should therefore be investigated before he is employed), is a gross materialist? What a scandal that the life of a child of God should be regulated by such a man! What a pity that a Christian soul should render super-

[1] *"Rationabile obsequium"*; Rom. XII, 1.

stitious obedience to such a despot! He finds that
the church is too chilly, and the patient no longer goes
to church. He finds that reading is fatiguing, and
the patient no longer reads. He declares the laws of
God unreasonable, and the patient separates himself
from God to please that man. But I will leave off.
I could say much more. Certainly, the reasonable
obedience of which the Apostle speaks has nothing
in common with this puerile fanaticism, which, under
the pretext of healing the body, places the soul beyond the pale of God's law, of duty, and sometimes
even of honor.[2]

The physician must be honest and conscientious;
otherwise his prescriptions will not be inspired by
truth and justice, but by passion, the current opinions of the day, and the vain caprices of the spirit
or of the heart. But we are to treat here not of the
duties of the physician, but of those of the sick.
Hence we presuppose that the practitioner is faithful to the sage formula of Hippocrates and is "honest in all the actions of his life," and knows but one
law, duty, and but one master, God. The patient
must, by his docility, aid the efforts of the physician, who seeks only to effect his cure and consequently to fulfill the duties of his vocation. Without
a doubt, this obedience, if it is religious, will be

[2] H. Perreyve, *La Journée des Malades,* 4th ed., pp. 155-
156.

inspired by higher motives; it will cause him to submit to illness with proper resignation, to accept the sacrifice involved with all its consequences, and to renounce his own will. But always it has for its aim to second the endeavors of the physician towards restoring the patient to the service of God and of his fellow-men.

Under these conditions, the physician, whilst safeguarding the interests of the soul in promoting those of the body, will permit all work compatible with the state of health of the patient, but will oppose imprudence and excesses. Alas! how many patients do not listen to medical advice and die before their time, thereby justifying the sinister axiom, "Man does not die, he kills himself"! How many great and saintly men, by excessive effort, cause the decay and collapse of their vital powers! We must join in the sorrowful regrets expressed by the Reverend P. Gratry, when he deplored the premature death of Father H. Perreyve, "that masterpiece of God," by reproaching him "with having sought death as much by want of discipline as by impetuous courage, like a soldier who is killed in advancing beyond his post." [3]

But here the voice of Henri Perreyve is heard, as it were, from the tomb, to remind us that the most reasonable obedience of the Christian "leaves

[3] Gratry, *Henri Perreyve*, 4th ed., 1873, p. 340.

him a part of his independence for generous boldness. There are cases where prudence loses its juris-
diction; they are the reserved cases of devotion [*i. e.,*
Christian charity]." [4]

A pious nun, who was commanded to keep to her
room because of sickness, wanted to leave it in order
to visit her beloved poor. "My children," said she
to the young nuns who wished to prevent her, "let
the physician fulfill his vocation, and we will fulfill
ours!"

What is to be said of such a response, and who
can oppose such devotion? Charity is as great as
the Heart of God, from which it proceeds: it is
without measure and knows no obstacles. The souls
that live for it aspire only to eternity, always ready
to sacrifice the interests of this miserable life, re-
peating the beautiful words of one such soul who
had been invited to rest: "Let us work now; we shall
have all eternity to rest."

[4] *La Journée des Malades,* p. 162.

# CHAPTER III

## PROFESSIONAL SECRECY

THE physician by reason of his office is the confidant of families. Nothing is hidden from him, who holds in his hands the health and life of the beloved members of the family, all its affairs are revealed to him, and he is permitted to penetrate the intimacy of the home and the deepest recesses of the heart. From this confidence arises professional secrecy; it is a duty imposed on the conscience of the physician, and is indispensable in the exercise of the art of medicine. It is prescribed not only by the moral law, but also by the interests and the honor of the profession. Hence we find this obligation in the ancient formula of Hippocrates,[1] which every practitioner must profess and which has been successfully adopted by various schools. The following is its text:

"Whatever I shall see or hear in society during the exercise of my profession, or even outside of the exercise of my profession, I shall keep secret in as

[1] Hippocrates (460–370 B.C. ?) is the "Father of Medicine," and the first to attempt the scientific establishment of the science of medicine. More than fifty works attributed to him have come down to us.

far as it must not be divulged, since I regard discretion as a duty of my profession."

In France the code of 1810 gave penal sanction to the traditional obligation of the secret, in Article 378: "Physicians, surgeons and other officers of health, as well as pharmacists, midwives and all other persons who either by their state or profession are depositaries of secrets confided to them, who, except in cases where the law obliges them to give information, shall reveal these secrets, shall be punishable by imprisonment from one to six months and by a fine of from 100 to 500 francs." [2] The legislator wished also to prevent, by just severities, "revelations which frequently tend to nothing less than compromising the persons from whom the secret was extracted, destroying in them that confidence, which became more harmful than useful, and causing those who find themselves in the same situation, to be the victims of their silence rather than of the indiscretion of another; and also to unmask the traitors

[2] "The common law did not recognize the relation of physician and patient as within the rule of privileged communications, but quite generally by statute this is the case. The privilege is allowed to be waived, where the patient sues the physician for malpractice (154 Mo. 112; 10 Ind. App. 5; 145 Ind. 238.) To make communications between physician and patient privileged, the relation of physician and patient must exist, the physician must be acting in his professional capacity, and must be actually a physician (154 N. Y. 355; 123 Ind. 384; 45 Hun. 307). Communications made to an assistant

among those whose state seems to oblige them to be benefactors and true consolers." [3]

By scrupulously observing secrecy concerning the facts known to him in the exercise of his profession, the physician, if guided by a correct conscience, will serve the combined interests of society and of the family, of public and private welfare.

Even though professional secrecy is a strict obligation for the physician, and, in principle at least, to be accepted without restriction or opposition, it must be admitted that, in practice, it is very complicated

come within the rule, but those made to a drug-clerk or a dentist do not (66 Mo. 588; 104 Mich. 563.) "The rule of exclusion under the statutes extends to information acquired while attending the patient in a professional character and which information was necessary to enable him to prescribe; this includes the patient's symptoms, the condition of his body, and the statements of others who are with him as well as communications from the lips of the patient (77 Ind. 203; 67 N. Y. 185; 110 Ia. 32; 91 Mo. App. 586.) The death of the patient does not remove the prohibition. And the assignee or personal representative of the patient may claim the privilege (80 N. Y. 281; 103 N. Y. 576; 111 N. Y. 120; 104 N. Y. 352; 99 N. Y. 56.) The privilege extends to the communications between the consulting physicians in the same case (99 Ia. 26; 103 N. Y. 573.)"—Chadman's *Cyclopedia of Law,* Vol. XI, Part II, The Law of Evidence, Ch. VI, Privileged Communications, sec. 1896; Physician and Patient, p. 257–258.

[3] *Exposé des Motifs du Code Pénal.* It would be much better for the commonweal if in the enforcement of our laws the sacred character of the professional secret were better observed.

and destined to raise serious difficulties in the future, as it has in the past. Prof. Tourdes,[4] who is an authority in this matter, says: "Beside the inflexible rule and the immutable duty of secrecy, there are possible exceptions, legal restrictions, and a casuistry which at times is very perplexing, because of the conflict between equally certain duties."

In certain cases the law abolishes professional secrecy and forces the physician to reveal what he knows. These exceptional cases, against which conscience has always protested, refer to crimes against the State.

In the case of criminal abortion, so frequent in our days, the physician is often in a quandary as to what course to pursue. We deem that, in general, he should keep silence, no matter how painful this duty may be.

Children who are the victims of violence which menaces their health or life, have a special right to the protection of the physician, and he must, after having taken care of them, report to the proper authorities the cause of their sickness, in order to prevent a repetition of the evil treatment. The insane and idiots, who are but grown-up children, have a right to the same protection.

In a case of poisoning which the physician alone discovers, he must report the crime, leaving the task

[4] *Encycl. Sc. Méd.*, 3e Série, t. VIII, pp. 418 sqq.

of finding the criminal to the authorities. The intervention of the physician here serves the interests of the patient and may save his life by preventing further attempts upon it. If he arrives after the death of the patient, he, by his report, at least sees to it that the crime is detected and justice is satisfied.

The report of births which every attending physician must make to the civil authorities by no means constitutes a violation of the professional secret within the limits and usage of the medical profession, and jurisprudence has imposed it to protect the children.

Some secrets are hard to keep in daily practice, especially when there is question of marriage. "If among our patients," says Dr. Gaide, "someone were afflicted with constitutional syphilis, which resists all treatment, yet did not hesitate to ask for the hand of a pure young girl, who is the joy of her family, and the father of this girl came to you with all confidence and asked you whether he could safely give his daughter to this man, who would infect her at the first contact or leave unto her children infected with that terrible malady, must we, I ask you, answer by a silence which may be misinterpreted, and thus become accomplices in a marriage whose fruits are sure to be deplorable? I do not think so and for my part declare that I should never have the courage to observe the law of silence in such a case; my conscience would cry out loudly and I should say without the least hesitation to the father of the girl: 'No, do not give your daughter to this man.' I should not add another word; nor should I feel that I had broken my professional secrecy; and if, by an impossible hypothesis, I should be punished for this deed, I should appeal to all fathers of families, and with my head held high, I should pity the tribunal which believed itself authorized to punish me for having preserved a woman and all her posterity from almost certain infection."

These beautiful words manifest a noble character, but they have not convinced our professors, who uphold the necessity of absolute secrecy, "because," says Dr. Dechambre, "the legal prescription is imperative, and admits of no exception, and we cannot exempt ourselves from it under the pretext that the confided secret will not always remain a secret; because every communication made by a patient to his physician by its very nature constitutes a necessary trust, which partakes of the nature of a secret."

Though bound by professional secrecy, the physician is not powerless in the face of objectionable marriages: he must use all his influence upon the afflicted party, and explain to him or her the impropriety of his conduct, appeal to his sense of honor, to the laws of hygiene, and especially try to induce him or her to adopt a temporizing policy which will postpone the marriage and perhaps make it impossible in the long run.

Conjugal syphilis, which is, alas! so frequent in our days, must be treated with the greatest discretion. But professional secrecy ceases when the venereal infection threatens to compromise the life of a child or the health of an innocent domestic in a family, and this condition frequently presents itself in the case of nurslings and wet nurses. Two cases may occur: The nurse is infected by the child, or the child is infected by the nurse.[5] In the former case, which is the more frequent, the absolute duty of the physician is to forbid further nursing, and to take all necessary measures to arrest the disease.

The parents of the child must make pecuniary reparation to the contaminated nurse; and she, in case of refusal, must receive from the attending physician a certificate as to the state and extent of the disease.

If the infection is caused by the nurse, the physician must forbid all further nursing, must take care of the nursling, inform the family, and impose upon the nurse the obligation of never again nursing any child under pain of being denounced, which will be the conscientious duty of the physician.

[5] A potent reason why mothers should nurse their own children if at all possible.

In a word, with the exception of the rare and legitimate cases indicated above, professional secrecy is a law and a duty of honor for the physician: but at times it is a painful duty, which would become insupportable without the generous inspirations of faith. We shall repeat here what we have said elsewhere: "The discreet physician guards all secrets well. What a burden does professional secrecy not impose upon us? What a torture may it not become, especially for souls who are aglow for justice and honor? How can the deceits practiced by society be borne without saying a word? This vicious man appears as the soul of honor, this libertine plays the prude, this despicable man seeks public esteem and obtains it—in a word, the whole sad comedy of human life. The physician knows and by lifting the mask can easily reveal the hidden turpitudes unknown to the world; but his conscience compels him to preserve these secrets, because he has faith in Him who sees all things. How weak the physician would really be, and how powerless to curb his indignation, were it not for his invincible faith in Divine Justice! At short range the crimes of this world are apt to disconcert the spirit of a good physician. But Divine Justice reassures him. It has an eternity in which to satisfy its claims: no fault will escape it and every virtue will find its recompense. In this hope the physician must live and fulfill his duties without weakening, waiting for those better days when God, the Eternal Truth, will give Himself entirely to the souls who have loved, served, and confessed Him here below." [6]

[6] *Le Médecin devant la Conscience,* Paris, 1890, pp. 168 sq.

# CHAPTER IV

## EPIDEMICS

EPIDEMICS, that terrible scourge of nations, constitute a proper field of activity and a solemn test for
the physician, who there finds opportunity to display
the virtues of his state and to employ all the resources of his zeal. Every one knows that the physician is charged with the defense of public health,
everyone believes him to be possessed of marvelous
resources, and all eyes are upon him, all hopes rest
upon him, as soon as an epidemic breaks out in
a city and begins to decimate the population. The
conscientious physician is lavish in his care for
others, without any thought of himself, and his generous efforts are at their height in repelling the assaults of death. This is for all a veritable battle-
field, and for many the field of honor, where "it is
good to conquer and also to die." Grave duties must
be fulfilled, be it in the name of conscience or in
the interest of the common weal; and we must here
examine them.

How can the physician reconcile professional secrecy, which he must keep inviolate, with the laws
of the sanitary police, which demand of the prac-

titioner that he reveal contagious diseases as soon as they appear, in order that their spread may be prevented? This is a serious question, which we cannot hope to solve. Having been mooted for a 100 years or more, it still awaits its solution. It causes a terrible conflict between the public interests, particular interests, and the conscience of the physician.

Formerly physicians were obliged only to report cases of pestilence, cholera, typhoid, and yellow fever. This obligation was freely accepted by physicians. In such cases recourse is never had to professional secrecy, but everyone seeks first of all to safeguard the public weal, which is the supreme law.

But diseases such as cholera and pestilence are exotic and of exceptional occurrence. The authorities have not hesitated to add to these other epidemic diseases as subject to report. Nay, they would apparently include all contagious diseases; but here physicians who are determined to uphold the dignity as well as the honor of their profession, have protested.

The obligation of medical secrecy depends upon conscience alone, and if it is successfully assaulted by law, it is doomed. With the physician's honor and dignity disappears the confidence of the patients, and that is the death of medical science.

It is only when contagious diseases are promptly reported that the prophylactic measures demanded by hygiene, can be applied and an epidemic arrested

in its origin; hence the making of reports is a very
commendable and excellent practice, but they can
never be demanded of the attending physician without infringing upon the professional secret which
constitutes his power and honor.

If conscience forbids the physician to betray the
secrets of his patients, it commands him on the other
hand to be lavish in his care and devotion to them.
Forced to live in a pestilential atmosphere in time
of epidemics, the physician more than others is exposed to the danger of contagion. Can he and must
he protect himself by minute precautions? The conscientious doctor has neither the time nor the desire
for such exertions, which seem to him almost a neglect of duty, for devotion means to forget oneself.
Frequent changes of clothes and washing the hands
and the face are in common use. All the antiseptics
in the world are apt to prove but a fragile armor
against disease. In the midst of the dangers of his
profession the physician is protected by the grace
of his state. He goes to the sick guided by duty and
strengthened by God.

The priest hesitates no more than the physician to
attend the sick in epidemics and to succor the dying;
and the physician would be unjust if he did not
esteem the faith and courage of the priest as highly
as his own.

Weakness or desertion in the face of the terrible

ravages of an epidemic would be for the physician like the desertion of a soldier in the face of the enemy, and would be disastrous in its consequences. It would deprive the sick of the necessary care, the authorities of an enlightened guidance, the families of salutary confidence, and, above all, it would be the signal of a general panic.

The physician (and with him often the priest, we are glad to say) is the soul of resistance to the murderous scourge of epidemics; it is he who gives the example of courage, of decisive and intelligent action and of perseverance; it is he who organizes and directs the efforts to stamp out the plague and assures their success. Hence he has not the right to fail in such a great and noble task; and though he does not always triumph over disease, he frequently has the honor of dying a glorious death.

Thanks be to God, the courage of the medical corps has been admirably sustained in every field of pain. They do not expect their reward from men, but are inspired solely by a high sense of duty. God grant that this spirit may endure and increase, and that the baneful breath of materialistic doctrines, striking at the heart of the younger generation, may never extinguish that zeal which constitutes the power and greatness of the medical profession, *i. e.,* love of humanity, the sacred fire of devotion, and, in a word, the love of Jesus Christ, the Great Physician.

# CHAPTER V

SURGERY, like medicine, seeks to heal and alleviate disease. By placing the lives of patients in danger or subjecting them to violent though transient torture, it sometimes contracts intimate relations with morality. At the present time, when the sense of responsibility is visibly declining and the value of human life is judged ·so unequally, it is more than ever necessary to insist upon the serious problems which present themselves in connection with surgical operations, both to the conscience of the physician and to that of the patient.

Every important operation entails for the physician a responsibility of which he must render an account, and which he must regard seriously. Most assuredly, an operation has for its purpose the amelioration of the patient's condition; it is not undertaken directly either for glory or for profit. The honest physician understands this duty and conforms his conduct thereto; he is not guided by fear of public opinion, nor does he seek to enhance the interests of his clients; he simply obeys his conscience.

If the patient is rich, the amputation must not be undertaken in order to obtain a big fee. If he is poor, the knife should not be used "for the sole pleasure of the art" or "to try one's hand." The interest of the patient, and not that of the surgeon, must be the supreme guide in all serious decisions.

Though this is not the place to treat the knotty question of the duties of surgeons, yet, led to the study of the duties of the patients who surrender themselves to the sharp instruments of the surgeon, we cannot conceal the fact that the surgeon, too, has formidable obligations and a terrible responsibility. Happy he who, conscious of his sublime task, casts aside worldly considerations, ignores the base calculations of self-interest, and does his duty under the sole inspiration of conscience.

If a physician judges an operation necessary and urgent, and if the operation offers a fair chance of being successful, thus saving the patient's life, with death as the sole alternative, is the patient obliged in conscience to submit? Must he undergo the operation?

The best theologians answer no; and it is impossible not to agree with them if, regardless of all extraneous motives, we wish to preserve the freedom of the human will.

No practitioner sincerely believes in the infallibility of science, and none would attempt to persuade public opinion that science is infallible. Is there not a daily accumulation of facts to demonstrate the shallowness and unreliability of our knowledge? Who among us is exempt from weakness and error? How often, when a case seemed desperate, to the confusion of the physician, nature caused a sudden and unexpected betterment and gave the lie to his somber and fatal prognosis.

The best-reasoned judgments of the best physicians are subject to revision. Sometimes an operation which seemed necessary and indispensable, is not undertaken, and the patient recovers. We remember the case of a patient whom the judgment of an illustrious doctor had irrevocably condemned to death, and who walks the streets to-day healthier perhaps than the doctor himself. This example carries with it an important lesson. The patient in question had long suffered from a tumor near the knee joint, which resisted all medical treatment and became more malignant; despairing of the case, the physician sent the patient to a surgeon as renowned for his moral qualities as for his professional ability. The case, after mature examination, seemed so grave to the worthy surgeon that he sent back the patient with the words: "The tumor is malignant and metastatic. Amputation of the thigh is necessary and urgent. Perform this immediately. If not, *it will be too late.*" The operation was not performed because of a categorical refusal on the part of the patient. To-day, six years after medical science sentenced him to death, the man is well and has no further need of medicine.

The calculations of the surgeon are often correct, but his hand does not avoid mistakes. Even the most skillful and experienced surgeon is not always safe from false movements and accidents. No one thinks of reproaching him for these inevitable failures. It happens that an operation which, from the standpoint of science, was defective, succeeds better than one which was conducted according to every rule.[1] The latter may appear satisfactory, nay, superb; and yet in some cases the patient dies a few days later. The cause of the failure is unknown or comes under the category of the unforeseen. A ligature, though well made, has not prevented a hemorrhage; a congestion by metastasis has occurred; accidents of septicemia have appeared, etc. It would take a long time, and would be unwise perhaps,

---

[1] How often does it not happen in rural communities and in cities, that girl mothers undertake abortion and succeed. Many, it is true, succumb to their imprudence, yet there are numerous cases where the medical profession is at a loss to account for the rapid recovery, when the operation was undertaken in an evidently unskillful manner and under the most unsanitary conditions.

to recount the "accidents" of surgery. In its relations with suffering humanity, medicine exists on faith and confidence; and its imperfections merely prove the weakness of human nature.

A patient who refuses to undergo an operation perhaps knows these facts; perhaps he mistrusts science and has but little faith in its resources. But the average man rarely has reasons of this sort. He merely recoils from the pain and the dangers of the operation, or dreads the loss of a member. He is afraid, and he has reason to be. Or, he may intrench himself behind his own will, without being obliged to give an account of the reasons for his determination. In that case, has medicine the right to dispose of his life? Is he not master of his own body, submissive to the secret designs of Providence?

Often, it is true, the patient offers blind, instinctive, and unreasoned resistance. In that case everything must be done to enlighten him. The doctor, the priest, the members of his family, and his friends should try to persuade him to submit, if the operation is likely to restore his activity and health, or if life depends upon it. Such grave reasons can, in certain cases, become imperious and influence the sick man's decision; but, be it well understood, they never entail a moral obligation to submit to an operation.

Operations which are not judged necessary may

never be undertaken, even though the patient insists. On this point the physician is the sole competent and responsible judge, and his conscience is sovereign; it cannot authorize a useless and dangerous operation, and it rigorously obliges him to abstain, no matter how painful the refusal may be, or how insistent the entreaties of the patient. In view of repeated insistence, and in difficult cases that present themselves in practice, he will do well to consult with colleagues in order to protect his conscience as well as to cover his responsibility.

# CHAPTER VI

## MEDICINES

THE physician has but one essential task to perform with suffering humanity: *to cure if possible, and always to alleviate pain.* We do not wish to exaggerate this task, but believe that it is great, useful, and legitimate. When a fellow-man is the prey of disease and writhes in the spasms of pain, the physician is there to give him aid and succor; and his intervention, which dries the tears and restores calm and joy, would almost make him proud did he not know that he is but the humble servant of the Most High, the instrument of His merciful goodness.

Nature furnishes us with more than one beneficent substance; it is the physician's task to apply these substances. Holy Scripture says: *"All healing is from God. The Most High hath created medicines out of the earth, and a wise man will not abhor them. The virtue of these things is come to the knowledge of man, and the Most High has given knowledge to man, that he may be honored in his wonders. By these he [the physician] shall cure and shall allay their pains, and of these the apothecary*

*shall make sweet confections and shall make up oint-*
*ments of health, and of his works there shall be no*
*end."* (Ecclus., XXXVIII, 2, 4, 6, 7.)

The use of medicines is, therefore, absolutely legitimate, and no one dreams of condemning it. But
since it is subject to abuse and may injure the body
which it is destined to heal, prudence requires that
it be exactly defined and carefully regulated.

The physician alone is called to prescribe proper
remedies for diseases. This is the essential point
which governs this question of medicine and the neglect of which causes so many errors, disappointments,
and irreparable accidents. The physician is prepared
by his studies and by his profession to recognize the
nature of the diseases which assail the body in thousands of forms and to know what remedies are indicated for each one of them; besides, he is best
able to judge of the constitution of the patient, to appreciate the condition of his strength, and to prescribe the nature and dosage of the medicine
which it is advisable for him to take.

No layman in the art of medicine knows the mys-
teries of the human organism, and no one would
pretend to know the cause and nature of any particular disease; and yet, by a singular contradiction,
everyone believes himself well instructed in the
secrets of hygiene, in the necessities of therapeutics,
and especially in the demands of his own tempera-

ment and the symptoms of the disease from which he suffers. Men are ignorant of the evil and yet pretend to cure it. If the physician interrogates the patient, instead of telling him his opinion, the patient will soon be dictating the prescription. Yet the patient's incompetence is natural and complete; and in following his own inspiration he often abstains from an appropriate remedy, or, what is worse, takes useless and even dangerous medicines. Such cases are of daily occurrence.

Many a one who wishes to cure his own disease hesitates to trust to his own lights and goes in search of a druggist; this, too, is a reprehensible practice. The druggist has no medical advice to give, and people should not demand it of him. It is wrongly supposed that those who prepare the drugs should know the ills for which they are used; people do not understand that it is the patient as well as the disease that the physician must study and understand, in order to establish a rational and efficacious treatment. Pharmacists as a rule do not know the science of medicine, and conscience commands them to refuse any kind of medical treatment; their sole rôle is to prepare the prescriptions issued by the physician, and we are glad to say that the majority are conscientious in this matter.

Need we speak of those patent medicines which are advertised in prospectuses, newspapers, and magazines as infallible cures for various diseases? Their prodigious success sufficiently characterizes human stupidity; but their actual value is nil. The publicity, accorded without restriction to the art of healing or rather to its counterfeits, certainly ought to be supervised and controlled, and the authorities would act wisely in putting an end to the exploitation of the public by charlatans, licensed or otherwise, who usurp or—what amounts to the same thing—profane the name of "doctor." The "harmless counsels of gossips" are less dangerous than those fraudulent advertisements, which penetrate every city and village. There are plenty of dupes to enrich the charlatans, and public health is never a consideration in the calculations of the latter.

The physician in treating the sick not only relies on his science, he is inspired by his conscience in the exercise of his art. He employs only known and tried remedies, and in the measure indicated by experience and the condition of his patient, he seeks only the interests of the latter and has but one object, the alleviation and cure of disease.

What conscientious physician would administer to his patient an unknown, secret remedy, whose effects had not been again and again tested and verified? or counsel excessive and harmful doses? or consider the human body as a mere *corpus vile* for experiments and seek above all to destroy the evil at the risk of killing the patient? The physician's dignity and honor severely forbid such aberrations, which, thank God, seldom occur. The physician wishes in the first place to save his patient; and love of science, no matter how developed, must never prevail in his heart over the love of his fellow-man, who is suffering and solicits his aid.

The physician must respond to the appeal of his patient, but he must not satisfy all his demands; he must follow the line of conduct traced for him by reason and science, and must, if necessary, resist the vain and dangerous requests of an enfeebled imagination. Occasionally a patient will demand remedies which are new or dangerous; the physician will refuse to prescribe them and, if it comes to the utmost, will refuse to assume any responsibility and hold himself in readiness to reduce all possible accidents to a minimum. Another will insistently demand certain advertised drugs, which are useless even if harmless. But what the physician must combat with energy and perseverance, in the interest of the treatment itself, is the inconstancy of the patient, who, tossed about between many caprices, anxious and disconcerted, wearies of a medicine before he has sufficiently used it, is incessantly disposed to change from one remedy to another, and is persuaded that the cure of his illness lies at the end of these deplorable tergiversations. The duty of the physician, on the contrary, is to maintain his prescriptions with order and continuity and to show that the return to health is only at the price of a treatment planned and applied with consistency and perseverance.

The physician owes his patients the truth, but he is not forbidden to use mental reservations and equivocal expressions, when health is in jeopardy and the interests of the patient demand it. When a nervous or weak patient demands dangerous or useless remedies, it is not always prudent to oppose him categorically or to meet his demands with sharp refusal, but modern educated physicians rarely resort to "bread pills" or "placebos." An intelligent psychotherapy yields far more satisfactory results without sacrificing the physician's self-respect.

# CHAPTER VII

## ANESTHETICS AND NARCOTICS

ANESTHETICS or *narcotics* are such substances as opium, morphine, cocaine, chloral, chloroform, ether, nitrous oxide, which possess the power of calming patients and soothing their pain. They have entered into the current practice of medicine and enjoy a legitimate vogue among the unfortunate patients. Their utility is incontestable, their necessity seems to us established; but has one the right to use them? Holy Scripture answers this question categorically: "The physician shall alleviate thy pains" (Ecclus. XXXVIII). Must we not admit, on the basis of experience, that nearly all diseases are accompanied by suffering and that the *immediate* task of the physician is not so much to cure the disease as to alleviate the patient's suffering?

The use of narcotics, therefore, is licit and excellent; but by very reason of their appreciable advantages, of their sovereign as well as swift action on pain, they are but too frequently and often fatally abused. This abuse is the more deplorable, as it attacks the nerve centers and the digestion, destroys the power of the intellect and will, and must, therefore, be condemned with the utmost rigor.

The first trial of a narcotic is so successful, brings so much relief and such a sweet repose, that the patient will almost certainly recur to it at the least sharp pain, or even to prevent pain, and thus little by little he becomes the victim of a fatal and incurable habit; since by becoming accustomed to them, the effect of these drugs becomes ever more tardy, the doses are gradually increased until they become too strong and gradually dangerous, and thus the body is slowly poisoned. This is the case of many unfortunates of our day—the history of their passion and death.

Pain is the great characteristic of human life, and we can never suppress it entirely, for it is part of our nature. When we consider it from the standpoint of faith, we realize that it is a consequence of original sin, that it follows us everywhere as a means of expiation, and that we must regard it as a fertile source of merit and virtue. From the standpoint of science, pain, which is inseparable from an organism that is subject to disease and death, can and must be assuaged, but it cannot be entirely suppressed; for it reveals the evil by various symptoms and thus makes it possible for the physician to apply the necessary remedy. *Pain is the cry of the suffering organ;* and medical art must always uphold the maxim: *"Sustine et abstine."* Patience and sobriety are two virtues which are recommended especially to the sick, but which hygiene impresses upon all.

Pain then must be combated, but with moderation. The safest and least dangerous narcotics should be chosen, administered in a moderate dose, and repeated when necessary, but, above all, care must be taken not to continue their use indefinitely, except in cases of extreme necessity. Within these wise limitations narcotics act efficaciously and render invaluable service.

One express reservation must, however, be made in the case of the dying. Narcotics, even when administered in small doses, have a strong tendency to plunge the dying into coma and thus deprive them of the power of recollecting themselves at the last moment. Hence it is prudent, nay, even necessary, not to put the dying to sleep, the more so as the pain which it is sought to combat by narcotics frequently diminishes or even disappears entirely towards the end. When the dying loudly demand narcotics, the physician should content himself with giving them light palliatives, which will suffice to assuage their pain, but will not deprive them of feeling. At times factitious means may be used, which will satisfy their excited imagination (a potion of sugar water or an injection of pure water).[1] The bishops of the province of Quebec at one of their councils condemned the administration of narcotics to the dying and defined the duty of physicians in the sense we have indicated: "Since the eternal fate of the soul," they say, "may depend upon the last moment of life, physicians must resolutely abstain from administering remedies which are by their nature apt to render the patients unconscious and rob them of the power of making acts of devotion, and to deprive them of the last merits, which they can still gain, and perhaps expose them to eternal death."

The first narcotic, as we know, was opium. Its action is energetic, but inferior to that of the new anesthetics. The ancients used and abused opium. There is no substance to which the system more easily accustoms itself; moreover, those who use it, quickly fall into the worst excesses. We know of cases where people have absorbed enormous quantities of this drug. But even though habit establishes a tolerance for the poison, it also entails grave general disorders, a weakening of the intellect and a decay of the vital powers. We know what opium smoking has done to China. England, which could

[1] The layman, and especially the priest, must be careful in accusing a doctor of having given a narcotic injection. Besides the factitious remedies, there are heart-stimulating injections, such as solutions of salt, nitroglycerine, strychnine, etc. Not every use of the needle means a narcotic injection.—Tr.

not have subjugated this immense empire by force of arms, has triumphed over it with cases of opium; but as a just retaliation it has itself not escaped the contagion. The English use opium especially under the form of "black drops" or laudanum. Young mothers who work in a factory leave their children at home and believe that they have taken care of them properly by giving them a dose of laudanum. This is a veritable crime. The use of opium in various forms has become a terrible scourge, and we know from innumerable cases as well as from a classic English work to what opium eaters finally come.[2]

After opium had been reduced to its elements and it was found that its alkaloids or salts are the truly active principles, medical science used the latter, and especially morphine, almost exclusively. We know that morphine can be applied locally and will alleviate pain more quickly and with greater certainty than opium; we also know that it is more completely absorbed subcutaneously than through the stomach, and that the most practical mode of administering it is by subcutaneous injection with a hypodermic syringe or needle. It is necessary to remark, however, that this alkaloid is as dangerous as it is efficacious, that wise moderation must be used in employing it, and that the physician alone has the neces-

[2] *Confessions of an English Opium Eater,* by Thomas De Quincey,

sary qualifications to give morphine injections.

The most excruciating pains (neuralgia, hepatic colic, cancer, etc., etc.) almost instantaneously disappear by the use of this marvelous drug. Therefore those who have once used it, recur to it on the occasion of the least indisposition, or even without any reason. Narcotics generally not only relieve pain, but cause sweet drowsiness, a sort of well-being, a truce to the preoccupations and the bustle of existence; their use becomes imperious and leads to abuse. It is the duty of the physician to prevent this disorder by regulating the use of the drug. He himself will make the injections suitable to relieve the pain, but will not renew them except in case of necessity, and he must not acquiesce in a dangerous mania or satisfy a vain caprice. His conscience must guard him against useless concessions. Certain chronic patients, who suffer veritable tortures, need a daily injection, especially in the evening, so that they can rest at night; the physician should not refuse this service, no matter how disagreeable it may be to him; he cannot leave it to anyone else except to a confrère or an intern. Morphine injections upon the dying, however, deprive them of sensation, and are extremely dangerous; hence they must not be made.

Sick persons, who have suffered much, and found relief in narcotics, sometimes will not listen to reason and constantly demand the drug with increasing

ardor. Use creates a need, and the need, becoming
in its turn a violent craving, creates morphinomania,
which undermines the body and the mind. Only too
often do these lovers of morphine find an accomplice
in their physician; they demand an injection, and
the physician complies. Later, either because of carelessness or from complacency, he abandons the needle
and the solution to the patient, thus giving him
the means to poison himself at his leisure. Such conduct is blameworthy, nay, criminal. Druggists who
sell this dangerous narcotic without a prescription
are guilty of a serious offense. In France, in the
eighties of the last century, a woman who suffered
from morphinomania became insane. She owed a
bill of 3,000 fr. at the conscienceless apothecary's
who had sold her the poison. The latter demanded
payment from the husband of the unfortunate
woman. The man indignantly refused to pay and
the case was taken to court. The court upheld the
man in his refusal and denied the payment of the
bill.[3]

We shall merely indicate in passing the excesses to
which the use of chloral and particularly of cocaine
leads, and pass to the dangers of chloroform, ether,
and other general anesthetics. These dangers still

[3] Anti-narcotic laws have done an immense amount of good
in stopping to a great extent the criminal traffic in narcotics.
Yet the abuse has not yet been fully stamped out.

exist, though in a diminished form, in spite of the great progress made in our days in anesthesia.

Total anesthesia should not be undertaken except for serious operations, and it would be imprudent to have recourse to it in cases of slight accidents or merely to overcome a passing pain. Furthermore, the patient must in all cases first be examined, and it must be ascertained that he does not suffer from any affection of the heart or lungs, for in that case anesthesia would be dangerous if not impracticable. Even in cases of individuals who are perfectly healthy, various accidents occur from time to time under the influence of chloroform ranging from syncope to death; and the occurrence of such dangers must recommend great caution in the choice of this means.[4]

We shall close this chapter with the wise and well-founded counsels formulated by the Fathers of the Council of Quebec, who declare:

"1. Physicians are allowed to put a person to sleep by means of narcotics, such as chloroform, morphine, etc., if it be but for a short time and there be no danger of death. There must also be sufficient reason, *e. g.*, to relieve violent pain or especially to perform a surgical operation.

2. This is permitted also in a desperate case, where

[4] See *Encycl. Americana.* Art. "Narcotics"; also "Analgesics"; Capellmann-Bergmann, *Pastoral-Medizin,* pp. 65–78.

there is some hope of saving the life of the patient.

3. It is never permitted in danger of death, for the sole purpose of taking away the feeling of pain.

4. Especially do we call the attention of physicians to the fact that they should make every effort to deter their patients from making use of narcotics which produce such pernicious effects."

# CHAPTER VIII

## MEDICAL EXAMINATIONS AND OPINIONS

THE courts frequently demand from physicians analyses and expert opinions calculated to enlighten the tribunal and to determine its sentence.

Such examinations must be made carefully and with every necessary precaution to avoid error. The conclusions of a physician called into court as an expert are decisive, since no one can correct them. Science establishes them, but duty must inspire them. The life and honor of the accused and the reputation of whole families depend upon them. Entire confidence is placed in the conscience of the physician, and this conscience must be a correct conscience, unprejudiced and free from bias, devoted only to the service of truth.

The analysis demanded by the courts must be complete. No reticence, no voluntary omission, is permitted, no matter what interests are at stake, or what the consequences may be. The physician must not take into account the interests of individuals, no matter how respectable they may be, but must look only to the interests of justice and truth.

The reports demanded of physicians by the courts contain professional judgments upon the facts submitted. The final conclusions must be clear, precise, and directly drawn from the facts. Frequently, these facts do not suffice to prove a crime; but taken together they constitute a grave presumption, which is almost equivalent to a proof and leads to conviction. The medical expert must conscientiously guard against introducing his own ideas into the exposé of facts as well as against leaving the exclusively technical domain in which he is supposed to be an authority; he must put aside all personal bias and not seek to impose his sentiments upon the court.

When the facts are obscure, uncertain, and insufficient to satisfy reason and procure a conviction, and when the conclusions, as a consequence, can only be approximate or doubtful, the physician must never hesitate to state them as his conscience presents them. It would be a criminal fault to sacrifice truth to self-love and to state simple probabilities as certain facts, in order to furnish a conclusive report. Here again duty must guard the physician against all weakness, and place upon his testimony the impress of truth, of the whole truth, and nothing but the truth.

What is the physician's duty if an examination is demanded not by a court, but by individuals? In other words, is he obliged to make his examination for his clients as rigorous and as complete as for the courts? This question is much controverted, and will be so for a long time to come, by reason of the various angles it presents. One of the most frequent and most useful analyses is that of urine, generally made in search of albumen, or sugar, or sedimentary salts. Aside from the necessary indications, which should guide treatment, and which must be very precise, it is of no possible use to the client to know *all* the substances that may happen to be in his urine, nor especially their proportions; and the physician who does not reveal these commits no fault. In most cases it is even prudent to confine oneself to mentioning only the useful information, because the patient is always prone to exaggerate his ills and long lists of unknown substances would quickly embark him on the indefinite road of foolish and imaginary terrors. Finally, in certain cases it is necessary to follow this latter practice, because a detailed analysis, imprudently shown to the client, might reveal facts not only useless, but disagreeable and sometimes even injurious. Thus we believe that no physician should indicate the presence of spermatozoa in the urine because the fact is, to say the least, useless and of no importance in the treatment.

To resume, then, it seems to us that the duty of the physician toward the administration of justice is, in this matter, without limit, *i. e.,* he owes the courts the whole truth; but in regard to his clients his duty is more restricted, and he must limit himself to serving their interests.

# CHAPTER IX

THE heart of every scholar, and especially that of
the physician, is necessarily divided between two
loves, the love of science and the love of his fellow-
men. These two praiseworthy sentiments, however,
are by no means equal, but the first should be subor-
dinate to the second according to the law of reason
and the teachings of faith. A science which would
refuse to descend from the high region of theory and
apply itself to the practical domain of facts, would
be a useless science. The truth is beautiful, but goodness is superior to it; or, let us rather say, truth is
excellent only when it becomes good and profitable
to all. Charity is that rare and celestial virtue without which *there is nothing,* in the energetic words of
St. Paul. This is the first and last word of science.

The physician's duties towards his patients are
determined in the light of well-established principles.
The demands of medicine take precedence over the
rights of science. Hence the patient must never be
considered as a mere object of experimentation nor
treated as such. The physician must have but one

purpose: to give relief and, if possible, to cure, and he may not, under any pretext whatever, sustain a disease which he is called upon to suppress, nor cause one which does not exist. The interest of his client must be supreme in his conscience and govern all his actions. As we have said elsewhere, "the love of science, no matter how highly developed, should never prevail in the heart of the physician over the love of his suffering brother who calls on him for aid."

These views are suggested by the simplest form of morality, and yet it does not seem useless to re-assert them in a time when the audacity of certain physiologists knows no bounds and the conduct of a goodly number of physicians no longer takes into account the nature of their profession, the character of their duties, and the value of human life. It must be admitted that these physicians, more desirous to satisfy their curiosity and to promote science than to observe the laws of morality, do not listen to the voice of conscience, are unmoved by the voice of humanity, and do not even notice the unworthiness of their procedure. How, then, can they be convinced of their error? How can they be made to understand the necessity of renouncing their adventurous and immoral experiments? By plainly stating the rights of the patient.

The love of neighbor is born of the love of God,

and those who deny the existence of the Creator cannot love their neighbor as themselves. They do not know true fraternity because they do not know the Father in Heaven. But even though charity be alien to them, justice remains, and its laws are applicable to all in their supreme rigor. Every man has the right to have his body respected. In like manner the patient has an absolute right, aside from operations necessary to cure or relieve him, not to be injured or tortured. As a consequence, the physician is not permitted to experiment upon a person, especially not without that person's formal consent. Now patients have never authorized those dangerous attempts which history records and conscience condemns; they have always been made surreptitiously, unknown to the unfortunate victims, and under the pretext of treatment. Let us hasten to add, in order that justice may be done to moral science, that the patient himself has no absolute right to dispose of his body as he may wish, and that his permission does not authorize the physician to make him the subject of experiments. Furthermore, it is sometimes impossible for the patient to give his permission; and we must here mention and condemn the attempts made on the weak-minded, idiots, and the insane, *i. e.*, upon patients who are as incapable of authorizing violence as they are of resisting it.

The scientists of the laboratory as a rule have a

very delicate sense of duty. Even most of the materialist persuasion, though they are devoid of all "prejudices" and hostile to all sentiment, still sufficiently respect their dignity—or public opinion—to abstain from imprudent experiments on their fellowmen. They restrict their interesting experiments *in anima vili.* Claude Bernard, with his great authority, always gave an example of this wise reserve, which we believe, has not ceased to be observed in France.

But in other countries, it must be admitted, certain physiologists have distinguished themselves by audacity in barbarous experiments. In America, in the seventies of the last century,[1] an over-enterprising scientist took it into his head to experiment on a poor woman. A tumor had penetrated the cranial bone. Without scruple he explored the brain substance and methodically and scientifically plunged in his probes. All devotion to science cannot excuse so savage a practice, and moral teaching condemns it most severely.

In the nineties a similar barbarism occurred in Germany. A savant had taken several babies and, confiding them to an old deaf and dumb woman, isolated them completely from the world in an inaccessible apartment, because he wished to leave their education to nature alone. The results were exactly what reason could have told him: the unfor-

[1] Surbled, *Le Cerveau,* 1890, p. 175.

tunate babies, deprived of the necessary care of a mother, and of all guidance and instruction, developed all the instincts of a beast; they could not speak. Fortunately for public morality, the affair became noised abroad, public opinion condemned such cruel barbarity, and a tribunal at Berlin cited the pseudo-scientist, who declared he had wished to make a "physiological experiment." He was duly punished.

Who would ever approve such unjustifiable experiments? We can only think with horror of their disastrous and irreparable consequences, of the tears and disgrace which they cause, of the long, miserable life which the imagination of a pseudo-scientist can prepare for innocent and frail infants, who, with ordinary education, might have become men and Christians.

Hypnotism deserves a special study. Experiments with this force are dangerous and should be forbidden. Surely no physician would be so unscrupulous as to make such experiments on healthy individuals, but ordinary people do not imitate this prudence. The great vogue which for some years attached to "animal magnetism" led many to have themselves put to sleep, or to put others to sleep, to submit to suggestions or to produce them, etc. In theaters, cafés, and various public halls séances frequently took place, which had such evil results that the public authorities in many places thought it best to forbid them. The prohibition should be made general. A distinguished physician, Prof. Guermonprez, of Lille, convincingly demonstrated the dangers of hypnotism before the Belgian Academy of Medicine; in our own practice there occurred a case of death as a result of a hypnotic séance.

At times physiological experiments present themselves ready-made to our eyes, be it by reason of a congenital anomaly, be it as the consequence of an accident or of a crime; in such cases the physician must make observations. The interests of the patient do not in this case oppose those of science; and the physician may honestly profit by the fortunate circumstances to study at first hand the activity of the living organs. But mark well, man is always but an object of observation and not of experimentation. This is a very important distinction. It was in this manner that, at the court of Charles I of England, Viscount Montgomery, who had, in his early youth, lost a number of ribs in his left side, so that his heart beat directly beneath the skin, furnished the famous Harvey with the opportunity of making a precious experiment. In our own days numerous physiologists have been able to verify important facts of cardiac circulation on a citizen of Hamburg, who suffered from a congenital fissure of the sternum, which permitted all the movements of the heart to be felt by the hand.

Everyone knows the story of Saint-Martin. This unfortunate Canadian, who had been injured by a shot in the region of the stomach, could be cured only at the price of a stomachal fistula; with good grace he submitted to the examinations of physiologists, and Beaumont, and later Smith, with his aid not only were able to study the activity of the gastric juices, but also conducted decisive experiments on the conditions of digestion.

Direct study of the brain has been made possible after traumatisms which took away a greater or less portion of the cranial bone. Blumenbach made interesting observations on a boy whose frontal bone was very much perforated and the brain was to a great extent covered only by a cutaneous cicatrix. Professor Mosso of Turin followed the movements and studied the circulation of the brain in three individuals whose cranial bones were either necrotic or accidentally broken.

There is no physician who cannot, in the course of his practice, constantly augment his store of scientific knowledge, learn new facts, establish old truths, and little by little observe a thousand details of physiology. Once we were able to observe a bare brain in an unfortunate man who was suffering from a large fracture of the skull, and to note some curious facts. We eagerly profited by this case, but we did not exploit it, content with observing whilst we were caring for the patient, and seeking above all to cure, in which it was our good fortune to succeed. But here we must admit that from rigorous duty to an imprudence, to a mistake, nay, even to a crime, the way is smooth and alluring. The stronger the temptation, the more energetically must it be resisted. Natural curiosity and love of science must not entice the physician to trangress the limits of simple observation or of simple and certainly harmless experiments, or, above all, to forget his medical and therapeutic duties.

# CHAPTER X

## MEDICAL EXPERIMENTS

Physicians have an ancient and sovereign rule which binds them in conscience and governs their practice: *"Primum non nocere."* No matter what happens, the treatment may be long, complicated, hard, even cruel, but it must never harm the patient, but must always have for its purpose to relieve his suffering and to cure him. This principle applies *a fortiori* to medical and surgical experimentation, which is only a patient and scrupulous trial of a medical or operative procedure, destined to replace older, less beneficial methods. Experiments must never be made for the sake of fame or profit or which may inflict useless torture upon the patients, but always purely for the sake of perfecting the art of healing and of rendering it, as much as possible, in accordance with a famous formula, "more sure, rapid, and mild."

Though surgery has always sought its inspiration in this wise maxim, yet it has more than once been subjected to grave reproaches, from professionals as well as from the laity. These reproaches were only too well founded and cannot be passed over in silence. Carried away by the interests of science and forgetting to some extent those of their patients, some surgeons have believed themselves authorized to make hazardous experiments, thereby uselessly imperiling the life or health of those whom it was their duty to cure. They have not always conformed to the essential conditions of the medical art. However, let us not be too severe upon these aberrations, but consider that, in practice, they are rare exceptions, and remember that, though the doctrine is plain and evident, the application of it is difficult and obscure and sometimes, as has been well said, it is easier to see one's duty than to do it.

This duty is clear and well understood by all. The physician cannot cure all the sick, but he should, as far as possible, relieve their misery, and not augment it; above all he must not kill them or shorten their fragile life by an inopportune and dangerous intervention. Nevertheless wisdom is not pusillanimity, and science supposes boldness. Conscience and reason must mutually enlighten each other, so that the physician may understand and draw correct conclusions in the complicated cases which daily occur in practice, and which must be solved immediately. To reserve and prudence, the product of reflection, the surgeon must join bold initiative, which arises from a sure understanding of himself and depends upon the physical and moral condition of the patient. It must be frankly stated that, if certain hazards were not permissible, progress would be impossible, and surgery would soon cease to exist.

In medicine the physician has at his disposal the observations of centuries to guide him in his practice; the effect of remedies is more precisely known, the way is surer, and the limits of experimentation are more restricted. Conscience can never tolerate the trial of new and dangerous products. An unknown substance may not be used in therapeutics before it has been submitted to a long and rigorous control in experiments upon animals; its use is permitted only when its nature, properties, and powers are known. The physician may never make a person, who demands succor from medical art, who seeks a cure or relief of suffering from medical science, the subject of experiments; he may not, without the loss of honor, nay, without crime, administer unknown, dangerous, or deadly drugs.

This rule is inflexible and becomes even more binding in conscience and really sacred, when one has to do with idiots, the insane, the incurable, or the dying, i. e., with those who are unable to defend in their own person the rights of humanity against such odious attempts.

We are glad to be able to declare, for the honor of science, that the illustrious Pasteur introduced his celebrated treatment of hydrophobia in accordance with the principles above enunciated. The antitoxin was tried upon animals long before it was applied to man. Without contesting the great value of the theory which presided over the learned researches of Pasteur, without entering into an examination of a still very obscure and much controverted question, and in accepting without discussion the proportion of deaths and cures as given by recent statistics, we feel that it is permissible to regret that untimely inoculations of the poison have been made on persons who had been bitten by suspected dogs, but certainly did not have hydrophobia, though they feared it. And we believe that the preventative inoculation of all dogs, prescribed by law, would perhaps be a more expeditious and better means of putting an end to hydrophobia.

For a long time the true nature of syphilis, that terrible disease, which often results from immoral relations and is their punishment, was unknown, and ancient physicians were powerless against its disastrous ravages. A better knowledge of this disease dates from the middle of the nineteenth century and is due to the labors of Ricord, Bassereau, Diday, Fournier, etc. The real discovery of the nature of this disease was not made until 1895, when Fritz

Schaudierer and Eric Hoffman discovered the causative organism, *spirochæta pallida*. This was followed by the diagnostic test of Bordet—Gengau—Wassermann.

We shall recall here only one of the most deplorable incidents. Ricord clearly recognized the duality of chancre. Some scientists, to verify the opinion of Ricord, inoculated paid subjects with the poison; and one of the most damnable inoculations was made in the hospital Saint-Louis upon an old blind man, who knew nothing of the matter. Was this not a monstrous crime? Yet it is not an isolated case in the history of syphilis; and everyone knows that the contagious quality of syphilitic blood, generally admitted to-day, was established by barbarous and unjustifiable inoculations of healthy and uninformed individuals.[1]

The rights and duties of experimentation are not well understood by all physicians, and it is by no means a rare occurrence to meet scientists who believe that their audacious, unjustifiable experiments are excused and authorized by their "love of science." Cases can be cited where the virus of certain contagious diseases (erysipelas, small-pox, etc.) has been inoculated into healthy subjects by curious and unscrupulous physicians. But the most cruel experiment was attempted in 1887 in Berlin by Doctors

[1] *Encycl. Americana, s. v.* "Syphilis."

Hahn and von Bergmann, and many still remember the profound emotion which was everywhere aroused when it was revealed to the French Academy of Medicine by Prof. Cornil, June 23, 1891.

While operating a woman for cancer, Dr. Hahn took a small particle of the extracted tumor and implanted it in another part of the body. This graft succeeded but too well, and two months later the unfortunate woman, after being operated upon for this new cancer, died of an acute disease. In spite of the scientific interest of the experiment, which Professor Cornil emphasized without palliating its horror, public opinion severely condemned the criminal experiment, for which there was not the least excuse.

We cannot conclude this study of experimentation without speaking of the application of hypnotism to the treatment of disease. Is hypnotism a true remedy? Is its use lawful? Is it moral? Perhaps the time has not yet come to pronounce definitely upon these points.[4]

Many physicians, allured by the vogue of hypnotism, have adopted it in their practice; but although it is not forbidden, it seems to us the greatest prudence should here prevail by reason of the profound obscurity which still envelops the brain and the psychical activity of man. Moreover, every-

[4] Lately renewed interest has been shown in this matter by reason of several alleged experiments in a Chicago hospital.

one knows that the practice of hynotism provokes serious disturbances of the nervous system. Most scientists also recognize the danger of passes and suggestions, and condemn their use on subjects who do not already show signs of nervous trouble. Many make still other important reservations, and Dr. Gilles de la Tourette writes: "From a medical point of view it is forbidden to hypnotize subjects who do not present symptoms of confirmed hysteria, unless we wish to develop numerous evils, which are more serious than those we undertake to cure." [5] Beneficial effects have been claimed for hypnotism in hysteria; but it is certainly well to ask whether it does not in its turn develop in neurotics profound disturbances, the danger of which cannot be compensated by the advantages gained.

[5] *L'hypnotisme et les états analogues au point de vue médico-légal,* p. 297.

# CHAPTER XI

INSURANCE constitutes a comparatively new form of assistance and provision for the future. It is spreading more and more and certainly deserves admiration and encouragement. But it has direct relations with morals, and its prosperity, nay, its very existence, is intimately bound up with the development of conscience. It can render service only in as far as it is supervised, controlled, and restrained within the boundaries traced by justice and respect for law.

*Fire insurance* is very popular. Its advantages are such as seduce and tempt perverse and avaricious souls and give opportunities for dishonest calculations. The courts are often called upon to punish dishonest persons who have become incendiaries in order to rob the insurance companies. The number of these crimes is constantly on the increase, and materialistic doctrines will certainly not put an end to them. The police are powerless. Conscience alone, by insisting on duty, can repress such crimes and make them impossible.

Insurance against death, commonly called *life insurance,* is lawful and in many regards moral. It gives security and confidence to the individual, protects the interests of all, defends the family against the terrible accidents which sometimes suddenly deprive them of their bread-winner. Zealous philanthropists do not cease to recommend life insurance to the laboring classes. Yet it is impossible not to see the dangers which it entails. What snares does it not set for the avaricious? To what hideous calculations has it not given rise? Our court records contain only too many examples, and the increasing abandonment of religion and morality presages no good for the future.

Insurance originated in England and there, in that supposedly religious and moral land, the abuses of this *per se* excellent institution are most frequent and serious. Heartless parents sometimes insure their children for high amounts, and then cold-bloodedly permit them to die of inanition and misery. The death which relieves these poor little creatures reveals no traces of violence and is most frequently reputed "natural" and insures a good income to the cunning and sinister plotters. Authorized calculations estimate the number of infanticides thus committed with impunity in Great Britain alone at 1,000 a year, and the law cannot reach them, nor can the insurance companies denounce them, since in these cases the establishment of the real cause of death is a difficult matter. It is to be feared that this "lucrative industry" will spread with the times and the morals of the day.[1]

The services which life insurance ordinarily demands of a physician are grave and difficult, and bind the conscience in such a manner that more than one doctor has refused to render them. Anxious to obtain all possible advantages from their operations and to avoid the least risk, the insurance company asks us to certify, after due examination, that the applicant is in good bodily health, free from all ailments and infirmities which might endanger his life. Two cases may present themselves: either the applicant is unknown to the examining physician, or he is or was his client. In the former case, no matter how carefully .the physician may examine the candidate, he cannot thoroughly know him in a half-hour, must depend upon his own testimony as to his constitution and antecedents, and is thus exposed to serious errors. In the latter case, professional secrecy .binds the physician with all its rigor, and we believe that he should refuse the certificate.[2] We know that not all practitioners have

[1] In Budapest and Belgrade, an association of married women insured their husbands, and then killed them (1926). (Translator.)

[2] American practice offers a practical solution. If the applicant comes to a doctor employed by the insurance company, he

such scruples, and that many find pleasure in obliging their friends and clients, and even advise them
"to make a good business deal." [3] It is the wish of
every conscientious physician that no physician
should abuse his calling or traffic at the expense of
his conscience by having valetudinarians and invalids obtain life insurance.

Rebuffed by conscientious doctors, insurance companies have hired physicians whose only care is to
satisfy their demands. Many companies, in their contracts, demand a certificate from the attending physician in case of death, stating the malady of which
the insured died.[4] In my opinion this clause violates
professional secrecy.

*Accident insurance* is also becoming more and
more popular. Employers and employees, it seems,
find therein equal protection. But though such a safe-

is bound in conscience to answer all questions truthfully and
submit to a thorough physical examination, which the doctor
is also obliged in conscience to make. Should the applicant be
ineligible, he should be informed of the fact so that he can
withdraw his application. The best method, however, is for
the applicant to consult his family physician before making
application. Some companies now issue insurance policies
without medical examination.—Tr.

[3] There can be nothing reprehensible in advising a healthy
man to take out life insurance before it is too late, or in advising
a healthy man, who is engaged in a dangerous occupation, to
take out insurance in order to protect his family.—Tr.

[4] This is demanded by law in all cases of death in the U. S. A.

guard be precious and commendable, its abuse is to be feared. We are not speaking here of a transient, individual, and unimportant abuse, but of a general abuse, which seeks to convert a social institution into an instrument of egotism and injustice. The employer has an important factory and an enormous responsibility. An insurance agent presents himself and says: [5] "For a small yearly premium we will relieve you of all your worry by insuring you and all your workers against accidents in your factory." The employer takes out the insurance and at the same time, being deceived by a very limited idea of his duties, may believe himself free from every further obligation. His workshops are narrow and badly ventilated, his tools worn and defective, his materials unsanitary and dangerous to health. What difference does it make? The insurance company will pay the damages for wounded or sick workmen. The machines are functioning, and immense belts cross the rooms in every direction, without guards. If an accident occurs, if a laborer, insufficiently protected against the risks of his vocation, is mutilated or killed, the insurance company will pay the damage. "But," someone will argue, "the employer certainly watches over his workmen in a general way and tries to protect them." We are glad to say that

[5] The methods of insurance agents are frequently dishonest, owing largely to the commission system.

he does. Nevertheless does not the insurance company induce him, does it not even make it lawful for him, to be somewhat careless, if he wishes to do nothing? Here is the great objection which truth obliges us to raise and which no sophism can refute.

The same facts exist outside the great industries in the various associations, and demonstrate the importance of conscience as a factor in insurance contracts. Will the insured employer manifest the same care in regard to the condition of his material as the one who is not insured? Are the pillars, boards, ropes, and ladders in his factory solid and well tested? If the employer is insured, a possible accident is not charged up to him, and his actual responsibility will ever be, no matter what may be said to the contrary, the only serious and efficacious guarantee of the laborer's welfare; it cannot be transferred or divided.

Chauffeurs are also insured. Why should they be denied a privilege which is extended to men in other vocations? If accidents are frequent, especially in large cities, the chauffeurs simply say, "We are insured." Is this new sort of insurance which, at least for the careless, strongly resembles a premium on accidents, lawful? Is it moral?

The carelessness and recklessness of chauffeurs, who need not worry as to the consequences of their

imprudences, does not protect the property of their
employers nor the welfare of their passengers, and
is certainly deplorable. But what is even more deplorable is the dishonesty of many who have a secret
understanding with each other and deliberately provoke accidents in order to collect indemnities. Some
years ago the Tribunal de la Seine, of Paris, sentenced an association of malefactors, composed of
cabmen, liverymen, insurance agents, and policemen,
who had successfully exploited a great number of
companies.

Pharmacists (who would believe it?) are insured like chauffeurs. Besides ordinary insurance,
they can take out a special insurance against any
accidents likely to occur in the exercise of their
profession. For a modest premium of $20 or $30
a year they are insured against risks of from
$10,000 to $15,000. If the owner of the pharmacy
or his apprentice makes a mistake in compounding
a prescription and patients, who should have been
cured, die of poison, the law-suits which follow do
not in the least disturb the apothecary, for any costs
and damages that may ensue are paid by the insurance company. Thus is a professional man protected,
his responsibility disappears, and the consequences
are incalcuable. What becomes of the bond required
by law? What significance has a diploma? The pharmacists suppress their obligations and their worries

at a small cost and attend to their pleasures, whilst they leave the multifarious cares of the prescription counter to their apprentices: they are insured! The profits of their business remain intact, only the duties disappear. We cannot see the morality of such an insurance, and we ask, how can it be reconciled with the law and with social justice?

Physicians' liability insurance protecting them against suits alleging malpractice are very generally carried by American practitioners.

*Maritime insurance* against the risks of the sea is the oldest form of insurance, and has occasioned crying abuses, since the verification of accidents is nearly always impossible. Maritime law has created a special word to designate the criminal methods which occasion or cause maritime accidents: *barratry,* which, in spite of the severe punishments attached thereto, still occurs with terrible frequency. It is well known that most cases of barratry are revolting; thousands of human lives have been sacrificed by avaricious shipowners, who knew their vessels to be damaged and rotten, but had previously insured them. Here we cannot blame the insurance companies, because, in protecting the ships and maritime mechandise, they are filling an essentially useful rôle. The facts of barratry pertain to the courts; they must be reported and prosecuted with extreme rigor.

Briefly then, insurance in all its forms is useful, and if applied by upright and conscientious men, renders inestimable social services. But, in an epoch when utilitarianism reigns supreme, when moral and religious principles no longer govern social life, it is necessary that the public authorities supervise and direct the insurance business closely. It would seem to us that certain forms of insurance should be positively forbidden, especially those which, far from guaranteeing life and health, endanger both, and outrage public morality.

# CHAPTER XII

THE science of medicine is far from being sovereign and infallible, nor can it cure all diseases; but God does not remain insensible to the sufferings of the sick, to the prayers of the faithful, and to the exigencies of His glory, and, whenever it pleases Him, intervenes to bring about an unhoped-for, unexpected, supernatural cure.

There are really *miraculous cures*, which transcend the resources of nature and the previsions of science. Miracles are, and always have been, the prerogative of God, the marvelous manifestation of His omnipotence and the adorable proof of His love. But we do not intend in this book to study the nature, the conditions, and the possibility of miracles; on this point we refer the reader to the works of the great masters, who will remove all doubt from an upright mind, and restrict ourselves to the consideration of certain miraculous cures, which have been observed, and to ascertain what part was played therein by the normal laws of nature and what was miraculous.

It cannot be denied that our ancestors often saw "miracles" in purely natural facts, which their minds, insufficiently enlightened by science or inadequately guided by logic, could not comprehend, but which the knowledge, since acquired by the human race, enables us to explain. Are we therefore authorized to believe that we, unlike the ancients, are infallible? Will the facts which to us seem inexplicable and supernatural be so considered by our descendants? Far from entertaining so presumptuous an opinion, we believe that the science of the future will revolutionize many conclusions, which we deem certain, and will demonstrate the insufficiency of many others. Such errors simply show our weakness, but they do not touch the real notion of a miracle, and leave the power of God intact.

There have been and always will be facts which science will never be able to explain, and which reason obliges us to qualify as miraculous. We do not refer to the miracles related in Sacred Scripture, which, aside from their divine character, offer unshakable certitude and occupy a place of their own in every Christian soul. As for the others, they are subject to scientific and prudent criticism, and only those must be admitted which are well established and rigorously tested. The interests of truth, which are also those of religion, strictly demand this.[1]

[1] All authors agree on this point and postulate many conditions to constitute a "miraculous cure." See especially Benedict

Miraculous cures can be publicly verified and are no rarer to-day than they were in the past. As a proof thereof we need only cite those that for more than fifty years have occurred at certain famous shrines, especially at Lourdes, through the intercession of the Blessed Virgin Mary. It is impossible to deny these numerous and outstanding miracles, in view of the testimony of the sick who were cured, of the crowds which witnessed the cures, and especially of the conscientious savants who examined and verified the facts.[2]

The most characteristic of these cures are those of cancerous tumors, some ulcerated, some not, tuberculosis of the lungs and of the bones,[3] and other well-known organic diseases which are the despair not only of the patient, but also of the physician. We may add those unfortunate infirmities which medical science declares incurable, such as atrophy, some kinds of deafness, or organic congenital aphasia etc. Cases of all these ills, of more or less long standing, which had resisted medical treatment,

XIV's great work, De Canonisatione Sanctorum, lib. IV, pars 1.

[2] See Dr. Boissarie, Lourdes, Histoire Médicale, Paris, 1891 ; Henri Lasserre, Notre Dame de Lourdes and Les Épisodes Miraculeux de Lourdes, 2 vols.; Georges Bertrin, Histoire Critique des Événements de Lourdes, and Un Miracle d' Aujourd'-hui, 1909.

[3] In Un Miracle d' Aujourd'hui, a cure of tuberculosis of the spine is scientifically examined.

were suddenly and radically healed, as if by a stroke from Heaven, contrary to all known laws of nature and despite the somber prognostications of the attending physicians. There you have genuine miracles. Medical examinations undertaken with the greatest care upon the miraculously healed, both before and after the cure, permit no reasonable doubt and force conviction upon the most incredulous.

There are those who attribute all miraculous facts to psychic influence and persuade themselves that nervous diseases and disturbances of the nervous system are the only diseases that receive relief or are cured at these famous shrines. This is an error, which must be abandoned. It is generally agreed that nervous as well as other diseases are susceptible of miraculous cures; but the most scrupulous attention and extreme reserve must be accorded to their examination, because they frequently yield to natural means and because, though we know the powerful action of the nerves upon the organism, we are ignorant of its limitations.

Hysteria is a Proteus of a thousand forms, which all the resources of therapeutics cannot seize and which nature alone sometimes succeeds in calming. Hysterical paralytics have recovered the use of their limbs through some violent commotion of the soul, e. g., in a fire. Epilepsy, so refractory to medical treatment, may be cured spontaneously; likewise mental alienation. An unexpected violent emotion may cause serious disturbances of the nervous system, but it sometimes also cures them.

The noted French physician Bouard had a patient who had suffered great financial reverses and whom no drug could arouse from a very alarming torpor. As a final prescription the doctor left this note: "Good for 40,000 francs at my banker's," and the patient recovered.

There have been numerous cures in the psycho-cerebral order which seemed extraordinary and quite beyond the resources of medical science, but which manifestly were attributable to some natural or psychic cause. No one would dream of contesting the evidence; but there are savants who believe themselves to be sincere, yet regard every sick person that goes to Lourdes as neurotic and attribute his or her recovery to hypnotism or suggestion. This is an unpardonable error, all the worse since the great days of pilgrimage, when the enthusiasm and piety are indescribable, when thousands of sick ardently implore God, the Blessed Virgin, and the Saints for help, are frequently noted for the scarcity or absence of all cures, and the miracles usually occur unexpectedly on the next day, or some days later, or even after the petitioners have returned home. Even more astonishing in these grand manifestations of faith, is the fact that sick women and children who are weak and impressionable, never suffer any fatal nervous mishap after all the fatigues of traveling, with the profound emotions which stir their whole being, and despite the fatiguing devotional exercises which they perform. How is it that nervous epidemics do not break out under such favoring circumstances? The fact that they do not, presents an insoluble problem for science and at the same time a striking proof of the sovereignty of the soul which rules those exhausted bodies, of the faith which animates the crowd, and of the Spirit of God which sustains them.

Hypnotic suggestion can produce salutary effects upon the sensibility and the morale of the sick, but it may also have no effect at all, or even aggravate the evil; and science has not yet determined the expediency of employing it. But the vogue which it formerly enjoyed led certain of its apostles to apply it to all human ills, nay, to see in it the only possible therapy. Dr. Liébeault of Nancy, for instance, in his book, *Thérapeutique Suggestive,* stated in all seriousness that he cured deafness, idiocy, anæmia, tuberculosis, hemorrhages, rheumatism, varicose veins, and in general all diseases by means of hypnotism.

Such a contention does not rest upon verified facts and hence does not deserve to be refuted. Supposing, *per impossibile,* that suggestion can explain the cure, hitherto attributed to divine intervention, of certain nervous diseases, it still remains certain that the cure of other diseases, which are known to be incurable, is truly miraculous.

But let us elevate our minds to a higher plane; let us humbly acknowledge our impotence and frankly proclaim that God is the only true physician. Whether the cure of the body is spontaneous, medical, or supernatural, it always proceeds from the sovereign Master, who has created us and upon whom we depend every moment of our existence. This conviction must awaken love and gratitude in our hearts. When nature seems powerless to stop a disease, when medical science has declared that disease incurable, the patient calls upon God, who can do all things, for help, and confidently awaits His intervention. My fellow-physicians, let us not depend upon such extremes, but let us always do our duty. In the rude perplexities of daily practice let us never forget to implore the aid of Heaven and to recommend to our patients the Great Physician, happy when this good Master deigns to make use of our weak hands to bring comfort to the patient and insure his cure. *Nos [damus] remedia, Deus [dat] salutem.*

# PART IV

# DEATH

# CHAPTER I

## SIGNS OF DEATH

DEATH is the sad accompaniment of life and, as it were, its necessary consequence. It is one of the most constant and most fully verified phenomena of existence; and yet public opinion, yielding to the foolish suggestions of the imagination and exaggerating the terrors of death, has sometimes refused to acknowledge its reality. Some have doubted the usually accepted proofs of death and zealously tried to find its true criterion.

Is there a sure and constant sign of death? No;[1] but there are numerous indications of unequal value, which, in their *ensemble,* permit us to recognize death with certainty. This or that sign is insufficient to guarantee death without danger of error; but the simultaneous appearance of the most important signs suffices to dispel all uncertainty. "The ideal for which we search," Tourdes very justly remarks, "is a pathognomonic sign, which is constant, unmistakable,

[1] In the 70's of the last century the Academy of Medicine of Paris founded a prize of 20,000 francs for anyone who would discover an infallible sign of death. To date this prize has not been claimed.

and easily recognized by every one; some place it in the extinction of this or that important function, others in some organic modification. Even though absolute certainty seems to be wanting to each of these signs, the problem has been solved and the *ensemble* or concurrence of certain characteristic signs furnishes the elements of a sure diagnosis." [2]

The best known signs of death are furnished by the general aspect of the face, the loss of sensibility and movement, of circulation and respiration, the lowering of the temperature, the condition of the eyes, stiffness (*rigor mortis*) and putrefaction. Let us take up these different signs successively.

The appearance of a corpse is not absolutely characteristic, for it varies according to age and the manner of death. The appearance of children quickly snatched away by some disease favors the illusion of life; for in viewing their restful and natural countenance, one would be tempted to say that they were sleeping.

Nevertheless in the generality of cases we must accord great weight to the dull and uniform pallor of the face, the thinness of the features, the open lips, the hanging of the lower jaw, the open or half-closed eyes, especially if to all these there is joined a relaxed attitude of the body. This attitude is deter-

[2] Art. *"Mort"* in *Dict. Encyclop. des Sc. Méd.* Also *Cyclopedia Americana, s. v.* "Death, Signs of."

mined by the laws of gravity, and is due to a total relaxation of the muscles. It must not be forgotten, however, that, as a result of certain diseases, this relaxation is absent, in which case a stiffness takes possession of the muscles (tetanus).

*Livid spots* and *blotches* of red, violet, or white, irregular in form, are produced by lying on the back and on those parts exposed to pressure by surrounding objects; they are due to an accumulation of blood and constitute a certain sign of death. If an incision is made on these spots, it will be noticed that the skin is bloodless at the periphery, but is gorged with blood deeper down. These post mortem lividities and putrefactive discolorations occur from four to five hours after death; unfortunately they manifest a variable intensity.

Absolute *insensibility* is a popular but rather equivocal sign of death. It is established in various ways (by friction, needle pricks, blistering plasters, cupping glasses and burns), to be done with due precaution, as life may not yet be extinct. Irritations of the skin are undertaken at points deemed very sensitive, on the breast, the nipples, the region of the stomach, the soles of the feet, the fingers or the toes. Burns give an especially valuable indication if inflicted with hot water, a hot iron, molten wax, or the flame of a candle. If they cause no reddening of the skin nor blister, the subject is dead. In death,

moreover, scarified cupping yields no blood. A strong
ligature of the finger or of some member causes
no swelling.

The *loss of movement,* like that of sensibility, is
a sure sign of death in the eyes of ordinary people;
but for the physician it has no value, except in so
far as it is corroborated by the noncontractility of
the muscles. It has been established beyond doubt
by the learned researches of Nysten and Hallé, that
the voluntary muscles remain contractile from seven
to eight hours after death. Hence if the application
of an induction current causes no movement of the
members, we can conclude that the subject is dead.

The *temperature* of a person in death agony often
goes below the normal mean, which is 98.6 Fahr. or
37 C., but never below 93.2 Fahr, or 34°C. Hence if
the thermometer repeatedly applied to the armpits
or the rectum shows a temperature below 82.4 Fahr.
or 28°C,[3] it can be asumed that the person is dead.
In these delicate explorations it should also be established, whether the temperature sinks gradually,
and the temperature of the surroundings must also
be taken into account. Equilibrium with the latter
will not take place until sixteen to twenty hours after
death.

[3] In certain cases of cholera temperatures as low as 76° F.
have been observed. *Cycl. Americana, s. v.* "Death." Capellmann-Bergmann, *Pastoral-Medizin,* p. 325.

The *suspension of respiration,* which people generally attempt to discover by holding the flame of a candle or a mirror before the lips, has not the value attributed to it by the common people; respiration may not always reveal itself even to the auscultation of the physician, because the respiratory movements are sometimes so feeble as to be imperceptible. Science reports many cases of hysteria and asphyxia where the mirror preserved its brilliancy, yet prolonged efforts resuscitated the supposedly dead persons.

The *complete cessation of the movements of the heart and of blood circulation* are of extreme importance, because it necessarily entails the cessation of all other functions; but it is not always easy to make sure of it.

The absence of circulation, as we have seen, is established by the application of the cupping glass and ligatures. If the subject is alive, a simple cupping will redden the skin and a scarified cupping will draw blood; the finger, if tightly tied, will swell and its extremity will become in turn red, violet, and almost black. These phenomena never appear in a corpse, but, on the other hand, they do not prove the complete cessation of circulation; all they prove conclusively is the cessation of capillary circulation.

The *pulse,* which indicates arterial circulation, ceases to beat after death; the arteries quickly empty themselves, and the veins are gorged with a blackish, more or less coagulated blood. In certain cases the pulse during life is almost imperceptible, sometimes filiform with notable intermissions; and it would be rash to conclude that a person is dead because his pulse is not plainly felt.

The cessation of the beating of the heart, ascertained by *palpation* and especially by *auscultation*, is a reliable sign of death; but we must guard against confusing suspensions of more or less duration with definite cessation. One should auscultate the cardiac region at every point where the heart-beats can be perceived, at least for five consecutive minutes. If these examinations, repeated a number of times at intervals of a few minutes, give no results, we can be sure that the person is dead.

The eyes also furnish numerous and sure signs, and recourse should always be had to them in doubtful cases. Aside from the open eyelids, death is marked by sunkenness and flaccidity of the eyeball due to the cessation of circulation and the evaporation of humidity. These phenomena are a characteristic and an indubitable sign of death. Mere insensibility of the cornea and of the optic nerve, on the contrary, has no great value, since it also exists in certain morbid states. At the same time the cornea loses its lustre and transparency, and is covered with a wrinkled layer, which results from epithelial desquamation. But, aside from the fact that these phenomena are more or less plain, we know that this layer is also observed in the dying. A more reliable sign is that the pupils become dilated, fixed, and insensible to all excitants. The sclerotic (white of the eye) becomes yellow some hours after death and shows a characteristic and gradually increasing dark spot. Finally, there is a complete discoloration of the retina, caused by the depletion of the central artery and its branches.[4]

*Rigor mortis* is a sign of death which is as dependable as it is ancient; unfortunately it does not set in immediately. Contractility of the muscles, as we have seen, continues for some hours after death and disappears only to give place to the *rigor mortis,* which results from a chemical change in muscle cells.

Muscular rigidity appears from three to four hours after death and requires from fifteen to twenty hours to involve the whole body; it then slowly diminishes until, after from thirty to forty hours, it disappears entirely.

*Putrefaction* is a characteristic sign of death. The rigidity of the body alone does not suffice to affirm that life has ceased, but its decomposition establishes death beyond all doubt. Putrefaction betrays itself from twenty-four to thirty-six hours after death by a greenish color of the skin of the abdomen,

[4] "Changes in the eye are corroborative rather than unique," *Cycl. Americana; s. v.* "Death."

by a softening of all the tissues, and by the production of a fetid gas. We need not describe the final disintegration of the organism, which destroys all the elements of our body and fulfills to the letter those profound words of Sacred Scripture, so frequently misunderstood by vain and perverse minds: *"Pulvis es, et in pulverem reverteris."*

# CHAPTER II

EVERY creature has an end. All life, confined within a definite course, has a fatal terminus, which is called death. Man also, in his present condition, is subject to death. Our existence on this earth is ephemeral; we are born to die. But though the origin of all human life is identical, the end is as varied as it is uncertain as to time.

> *"Mille modis morimur mortales, nascimur uno;*
> *Una via est vitae, moriendi mille figurae."*

Sometimes the longest life has the simplest termination. The person who has reached an extreme old age, dies slowly, as it were, piece-meal. The organs, worn out and fatigued, perform their functions imperfectly, and gradually cease functioning altogether. The nervous system, which is the most delicate as well as the most important part of the body, is attacked before all others; the senses suffer the first irremediable decline. The sight grows dim, the hearing dull and more and more insensible to sound; touch and smell lose their acuteness and

245

delicacy; even the taste sometimes becomes blunted. Little by little the cerebral functions are endangered, because they are deprived of the support of the senses; the memory becomes less faithful and finally vanishes; the imagination declines and becomes atrophied, and the sense of correlation disappears. The intelligence decreases and finally becomes nil; and its loss is the more noticeable, since the instinct of habit remains alive for a long time.

The interrelational activity of the organs decreases through atrophy and rigidity of the muscles. Strength deserts the old. Their walk is laborious, their movements are slow and difficult, their back is bent, their legs knock against each other, and their voice is cracked. Muscular activity no longer responds to the orders of the will. The body becomes emaciated, the skin dry, parchment-like and brownish, the eyes lose their luster, and the face its expression. Everything about an aged man reveals exhaustion and the near approach of death; he is no more than the shadow of a man; but he is not yet a corpse.

The organic functions continue to operate, though in a weakened form. The body lives and repairs its languishing forces. But soon the interior life is in its turn attacked; digestion stops, assimilation ceases, the secretions diminish and dry up, the circulation is impeded and finally ceases; the heart is disturbed and at last stops beating. That is the last moment of a long existence. Life is possible only as long as the heart beats and sends its liquid nourishment to all the organs. The heart is the *ultimum moriens,* the organ that dies last.

Such is the death of those whom disease has spared, the death of old age or senility, which is caused by the progress of decrepitude and the cycle of vital evolution. But few people die of old age. Most frequently it is a disease which either gradually or suddenly attacks a vital part of the organism and puts an end to human existence. But disease does not always depend on exterior circumstances or surrounding influences; it frequently arises within the body itself, which harbors the germs of death, or, to be more exact, destroys itself by its own forces. Hence disease is not an independent, positive entity, but rather a serious disturbance of the harmony of the various functions; it is, as pathologists teach, one of the forms of living activity, a simple modality of life. Life must be considered as a preparation for death, and the human body, as St. Paul truly says, is nothing more than "a body of death."

Bichat expressed the opinion that death occurs only in consequence of a change in one of the three essential organs (brain, heart, and lungs) which constitute the "vital tripod." This may still be accepted as covering the great majority of cases.

One of the most frequent causes of death is lung

trouble. In pneumonia, bronchitis, tuberculosis, various diseases of the throat, of the larynx, and of the respiratory system, by which entry of air and the oxidation of the blood are impeded and impaired, a gradually increasing asphyxiation is the cause of death.

Since the heart maintains relations with the other organs, and performs an interrupted and prodigious amount of labor, the diseases to which it is subject are as serious as they are numerous. A simple syncope may be fatal. Every severe hemorrhage affects the heart as well as the brain; the skin assumes a wax-like color, becomes cold and covered with perspiration, respiration is labored and gasping, vertigo appears, the patient sees flashes of light, the pulse is less and less perceptible, and finally the heart ceases to beat.

Death may also result from any of the diseases which endanger the brain (congestions, hemorrhages, closure of the arteries, etc.) and from those which, by vitiating the blood, affect the general process of nutrition and especially that of the nervous system, which is so fragile and yet so necessary. Under this head we must put fevers of every kind, infections and epidemic diseases, and all diatheses. Finally certain chronic affections of the digestive tract may obstruct the passage of its contents or exhaust the juices necessary for the solution of food, and thus make the absorption of the latter impossible, whereupon nutrition languishes and the unfortunate patient dies of weakness and inanition.

Death is ordinarily preceded by a number of phenomena which at the same time prepare the way for and announce the end of life. To these we give the name of the moribund state. Since these phenomena are varied and of very unequal value, we shall now point out those which are constant and precise enough to leave no doubt that the last hour has come.

The countenance of a dying person is pale and earthy grey, the features become drawn, the nose pointed, the eyes lose their lustre and become *veiled,* insensible to all that happens, the mouth is open or half-open and seems to beg for air, permitting the reddened and dry mucuous membrane of the tongue and the gums to be seen. The latter are frequently coated with a dark crust, which is also to be found at the nasal entrances. That is the description of a person in his last agony, as it presents itself to the eyes of the physician and the priest, who, called by duty, must contemplate it almost daily (*facies hippocratica*).

At the same time the respiration becomes labored, its movements are intermittent, gasping, and of unequal force, and even from a distance can be heard a sinister noise, the death rattle, which is caused by the presence of mucuous secretion in the larynx and trachea, which the patient can no longer expectorate, and which impedes respiration; this is the so-called *death rattle,* which increases up to the last breath.

The attitude of the dying is so variable that it cannot furnish a reliable indication of approaching death. At times it reveals the complete prostration of all vital forces; the patient lies on his bed of suffering, inert and as if paralyzed. Again he may be the victim of violent agitations or convulsive spasms, either partial or general. Between these two extremes intermediary forms may be observed. Frequently there are ceaseless, instinctive movements of the hands as if they were trying to pick up some imaginary object on the bed-cover or to draw the covers over the breast; this curious automatism has received the name of *carphology* or *floccilation.*

The temperature is unreliable as a criterion of approaching death. Most dying persons feel their temperature decrease and end in relative algidity; but there are exceptions. Frequently the skin is cold and covered with profuse perspiration; sometimes, also, it is dry and burning hot; in both cases the thermometer may contradict the estimate of the hand. During the algid period of cholera the rectal temperature is always from 38° to 39°C., (100.4° to 102.2° Fahr.) whilst the extremities are icy cold. In tetanus, the temperature may reach 41° and 42°C. (105.8° to 107.6° Fahr.) without necessarily prognosticating a fatal issue; even after death it sometimes rises from one to two degrees.

The pulse is no more characteristic than the animal temperature. A rapid pulse, beating more than 150 strokes a minute, may be a disquieting sign, but it alone does not presage death. Often a weakening of the pulsations is noticed. Auscultation and palpation of the heart give but uncertain and confused signs.

The state of the brain is variable, sometimes plunging the patient into a deep sleep and absolute insensibility (*coma*), and again leaving him more or less in the possession of his intellectual faculties. The importance of this question from a moral and religious standpoint has induced us to reserve it for a later chapter.

As we have seen, the death agony presents no uniformity, but differs according to the nature of the illness. It is not the same in the case of the aged as in that of the adult or the child. It may last for several hours, for a whole day, or even for several days, or it may be over in a half-hour or less. We have mentioned the signs which are to some extent constant, and the *ensemble* of these signs is of great value to the physician, since it permits him to inform the family of the extreme danger of the patient. The priest, too, can find in it a useful hint. Even the friends of the family, if instructed in this matter, will never have to reproach themselves that they did not warn those about the sick person; and thus they will frequently avoid recriminations after an unforeseen death.

Unfortunately, this premonitory agony does not always occur, especially if one of the three primary functions of the organism (innervation, circulation, respiration) is suddenly suppressed. The healthy person then passes instantaneously from life to death.

# CHAPTER III

WHEN some unfortunate person drops down lifeless and suddenly loses all sensibility and movement, we believe him to be the victim of a *sudden death,* but sometimes death is only apparent. The two states are fundamentally very dissimilar, because the one is real death and the other latent life, but resemble each other closely because of the disappearance of every sign of animal life, and for that reason we shall consider them together in this chapter.

Sudden death may be occasioned by certain exterior and accidental causes (a fall, a blow, a stroke of lightning, traumatisms, etc.), which attack the heart, the lungs, or the brain.

A violent emotion sometimes suffices to stop the movements of the heart and to cause a mortal syncope. Pope Leo X died of joy, and many people have been known to die of fright.

In health the heart must bear the reactions of the affections of the soul and its action may be inhibited. Though well protected, it is a fragile organ. A violent blow, a seemingly slight wound, may stop its

action. A rupture is fatal. Interior lesions often lead
to sudden death. Sometimes the heart sends blood
clots (*embolisms*) to the lungs or brain, which obstruct the circulation of these essential organs and
thus cause sudden death. Cerebral apoplexy is always serious and frequently comes like a stroke of
lightning. The rupture of an aneurism, a severe
hemorrhage, whether internal or external, can cause
sudden death. Again the cause may escape an ordinary routine examination, as for example in affections of the thymus.

Sudden death is characterized by the simultaneous
cessation of the vegetative life and of the animal
functions; the trance, which is sometimes mistaken
for sudden death, is distinguished therefrom by the
continuation of nutritive life. A careful examination must be made in cases of doubt to discover the
obscure traces of life in the organs by ·making use
of those modern discoveries which have established
the true signs of death.

The trance state is constituted by a sort of complete depression. The body is relaxed, inert, and
plunged in a deep sleep, comparable to death;
not the least movement is noticeable, not even in
the thorax. The various excitants, to which recourse
is usually had to allay this disquieting stupor, remain without effect and cause the counterfeit death
to appear real. We can always attribute the numer-

ous states of the organism which simulate death to one of the organs that constitute the "tripod of life."

The most characteristic trance states are those called *lethargic* and *cataleptic,* which sometimes last for days, nay, weeks. Besides these great crises of hysteria we must cite, in the line of cerebral affections, congestion, violent emotions, apoplexy, epileptic coma, drunkenness, a lightning stroke, certain narcotic poisonings, etc.

The trance which originates in the heart is well known and of frequent occurrence; it is called *syncope* and is occasioned by violent and unexpected physical or moral emotions closely related to the nervous system. The sense of feeling as well as the emotions seem to have disappeared, the temperature of the body drops, and the skin assumes a pale and livid hue. But there is no reason to doubt the existence of life, if insensibility is complete, if respiration is imperceptible, and circulation is not suspended; an attentive examination will show the continuance of circulation. The heart-beats continue, though feeble, attenuated, and less frequent than usual, but still plain enough to reach the ear when applied to the precordial region.

*Asphyxia,* which consists in the suppression of oxygenation as a result of the suspension of respiration, may, if prolonged, terminate in a serious syncope and cause apparent death or trance. It occurs as the consequence of strangulation, drowning, the inhalation of gases, which exclude oxygen—in a word, whenever respirable air no longer has access to the lungs. It may be of exceptionally long duration. Ancient Greek divers were able, by practice and habit, voluntarily to suspend breathing and to sustain asphyxia for quite a time. Drowned persons have been revived after many hours of absolute insensibility; the same is true of unfortunate miners and firemen who were asphyxiated by coal gas or smoke. Life in these cases was indubitably preserved by the persistence of cardiac pulsations. The heart is always the king of life, the *ultimum moriens*.

This last spark, this final residue of life, is not visible to the eyes of ordinary persons and for a long time escaped even the notice of physicians. When a body was inert and insensible to all excitation, the old practitioners concluded that it was dead. The annals of science, which record the progress as well as the errors of the human mind, report numerous cases where a trance was mistaken for real death, and some instances where the victims were buried alive.[1]

The known cases are sad and startling. On an

[1] "It is certain that the thought of being buried alive and, perhaps, regaining consciousness in the grave, is terrible; but it is just as certain that the frequency of this occurrence has always been considerably exaggerated." (Capellmann-Bergmann, *Pastoral-Medizin* p. 327).

estate in the department of Charente-Inférieure, France, an old keeper had died. The corpse was laid on a straw mattress; the final preparations for burial were made; at his feet was placed a vessel of holy water with a spray of boxwood and a lighted candle. An old lady of the village was left there to keep the deathwatch. She fell asleep and towards midnight awoke to find herself surrounded by flames. She dashed from the building and called for help. The neighbors came a-running to extinguish the flames which had set the old woman's clothes on fire. Suddenly, to their horror, they saw a naked man stagger from the house, presenting some severe burns; it was the dead man! While the good woman slept, a spark from the candle had set the straw mattress afire and awakened her from her sleep and the keeper from his trance. He was cured of his so-to-speak providential wounds.

On October 15, 1842, a farmer in the neighborhood of Neufchâtel (Seine-Inférieure), went to his hayloft to sleep. The next morning his wife found him dead. On the following day, as the coffin was being carried down a ladder, one of the rungs broke and precipitated the coffin to the ground. It burst open and the dead man, who was not dead at all, but only in a trance, awoke and emerged from his shroud to the horror of the bystanders.

About the same time an inhabitant of Nantes died

after a long illness. During the burial ceremonies at church the "dead man" moved violently in his coffin. The people hurried to aid him and bring him home, and soon he regained consciousness. When the resuscitated man was requested to pay the expenses of his premature funeral, he sent the bill to his heirs; the consequence was a law-suit, which for some time entertained the public.

Cardinal Donnet of Bordeaux was almost buried alive, as he himself one day related in the French Senate.

The error of the celebrated accoucheur Peu is well known. He was called to a pregnant woman, who was in a state of absolute insensibility. He examined her carefully and pronounced her dead. Being requested to perform the Cæsarian operation in order to save the child, he inserted the knife into her abdomen, and during the operation the woman emerged from her trance and regained her senses.

About seventy-five years ago, in the village of Eymes (Dordogne), a man who suffered from a very painful insomnia and was gradually losing his strength, went to a doctor, who prescribed a preparation of opium. "This remedy," said the physician, "will cure your trouble, but be sure to use it only moderately and obey the instructions." The man, who was convinced, like all rustics, that the medicine would work better the more he took of it, swallowed it all at one time. He fell into a sleep and after about twenty-four hours his family became anxious and tried to rouse him, but to no purpose. The physician who was called in established the algidity of the corpse and its complete insensibility, as well as the absence of the pulse; for safety's sake he cut two arteries of the arm and obtained only one or two drops of thick, blackish blood; he thereupon pronounced the man dead and the burial took place. After a few days, a vague rumor spread concerning the imprudence of the patient, who had taken an excessive quantity of the narcotic. The authorities investigated and ordered the exhumation of the body. A frightful spectacle was witnessed. The unfortunate man had turned around in his coffin. His shroud was covered with blood which had escaped from his opened arteries. His face was convulsively contracted, and the contracted muscles plainly betrayed the long and horrible agony which had preceded death.

Such facts are heart-rending, but thanks be to God, no longer occur in our days; the most recent instances date to sixty years ago. But the horror of their memory has long haunted the public, and an exaggerated fear of their return was not the least contributing cause in the establishment of various

measures destined to prevent such premature burials.
In many countries mortuary chapels were built to
receive and keep the corpses of the deceased for
some time. The cord of a little bell was carefully
tied to the hands of the deceased; but it never gave
the least sound, and no one has ever seen any of the
corpses placed in these depositories come to life after
a medical certification of death. Police regulations,
too, which forbid autopsies and burials before
twenty-four hours after the declaration of death,
have the same purpose of wise precaution; but what
dissipates all uncertainty and fear, is the definite
stopping of the heart-beats, which constitutes the
best sign of real death and which a medical examination will reveal. Thanks to this almost infallible
criterion, we can to-day avoid the most deplorable of
errors. Further protection is afforded by the now
common practice of embalming corpses before burial.

It is superfluous to remark that all the cases of
apparent death which have recently deceived laymen
as well as physicians were attributable to cerebral affections (lethargy, hysteria, narcotic intoxication).
Hence, whenever these affections occur, the physician
will naturally be on the alert and in case of necessity,
will have recourse to all the tests in common use and
will wait. Not the least doubt need, generally speaking, be entertained of the death of patients who have
succumbed to acute or chronic diseases of the lungs,

heart, liver, kidneys, etc., because the natural course of the disease as well as the symptoms of the last hour, the last agony, etc., prepare and clearly foreshadow the end.

# CHAPTER IV

## CARE OF THE DYING

THE last hour has sounded; the patient is in his last agony. Now more than ever, is the time to surround him with friendly and attentive care and to attend to his needs; no human being should be left to die alone.

It is undoubtedly true "that medical science is powerless to save his life"; but it can still help him and give him relief in his painful passage from this life to eternity. Those are seriously mistaken who, in such a case, say, "There is nothing more to be done." The art of medicine is not only the art of curing, but also, and above all, the art of relieving suffering. And duty dictates to the physician that he must fill this latter rôle in desperate cases, even if charity did not command him to assist the dying to the very end.

Another reason forbids the abandonment of the sick and renders the presence of the physician almost necessary at the supreme moment. As death approaches, its premonitory symptoms are apt to drive those about the patient to despair and render them helpless. They also are in need of comfort and

counsel; they are broken-hearted, agitated, disconcerted, and can, by their negligence and ill-concealed
grief, aggravate the final trial of the dying person.
The physician has full authority to remedy the evil;
his mere presence, his cool, collected, but always
sympathetic attitude is calculated to reassure those
about the dying person. He can dictate their conduct
and spare the patient the too noisy outbreak of
family grief and guarantee him the necessary care.
If he leaves before the final moment, even though he
gives the very best advice, he abandons the relatives
to discouragement and despair. Frightened by the
idea of the inevitable end, crushed by the lamentable
sight of the dear person in his last agony, they are
stupefied and powerless, incapable of giving aid and,
losing all self-restraint, often can do no more than
fill the room with their sighs and lamentations.

The physician, therefore, has his rightful place
at the bed of the dying, but he must not take it except in as far as it is willingly yielded to him by the
family; his ministry, be it ever so sublime, should
not intrude itself. Prudence and tact will indicate
what course of conduct to follow. His absence may,
of course, be justified by reason of the condition of
the patient, by the opinion of those about him, or
by the demands of other clients.

In every case, however, the dying person retains
the right to efficient help, and the physician must

always give some person about the dying the instructions necessary to insure this aid. These persons would neglect the most serious of duties in not lavishing on the patient at this hour all possible care and attention.

Overwhelmed by disease, the patient is often the prey to a dull fever, and lies in his bed powerless, nay, almost lifeless. A cold sweat breaks out and stands in drops on his brow. Is it not the duty of some friend's hand to wipe off this sweat and to refresh that brow? Compresses, dipped in pure or acidulated water, and applied to the brow, will often afford some comfort.

Thirst is the most frequent and the most poignant suffering of the dying; it should be unhesitatingly and constantly alleviated. Fresh or sweetened water, or water mixed with a little wine or whiskey, should be given, but only in small quantities, since deglutition becomes painful. Frequently the patient can no longer swallow; then pains should be taken to cool at least his mouth and lips. The mouth and lips are carefully moistened with a few drops of liquid applied either with a cloth or a soft feather.

In the meantime asphyxia is making rapid progress, and most frequently puts an end to the agony of the dying. All efforts should tend to combat this anxious difficulty of breathing and to facilitate the access of air in every possible manner. The room should be well ventilated, and only a few indispensable persons should be present; the patient should lie or sit supported by pillows, lightly covered and divested of all useless clothing or appliances, which would interfere with the free movement of the ribs and respiratory organs.

As the available lung area becomes more restricted, the patient's strength diminishes, and his intellectual powers weaken. Before long the face betrays prostration. The eyes become veiled, the faculty of hearing is lost, sensibility grows obtuse; vegetative life alone exists. Fortunately, the science of medicine possesses precious resources which enable it successfully to combat this prostration and to reanimate the nervous activity of the patient for some minutes at least; a subcutaneous injection [1] of ether or caffeine is the remedy mostly used, The torpor is quickly dissipated, the face becomes animated and the intellect more or less regains possession of itself. This return to life, sometimes unexpected, in certain cases permits the manifestation of a last desire or will, and it is always favorable to the general state of the patient by dissipating the oppression and torture occasioned by the waning of his strength. Patients who were almost dead have been seen to awaken, thanks to this artificial means, and make

[1] Professor Peter prefers a deep injection into the muscular tissues.

good use of the respite thus obtained, in settling their affairs or bidding the last farewell to their dear ones. Hence it is permissible, lawful, nay even recommendable, to have recourse to injections of ether or caffeine every time that a physician expects some benefit therefrom for the patient.

On the other hand, injections of large doses of morphine or any other narcotic are rigorously forbidden during the last hours of life. There is usually no need of them, for the dying person quickly loses all sensibility and consciousness of pain. If, as may happen in some cases, the suffering is excessive, the administration of a light sedative is perfectly authorized, but not that of an anesthetic capable of making the patient completely lose the use of his senses, and therefore the benefit of pain. This is the authorized teaching of the Fathers of the Council of Quebec, to which we subscribe without reserve. The following are the considerations upon which the bishops of Canada relied: "Since the eternal fate of the soul depends upon the last hours of life, physicians must absolutely refrain from administering remedies which, by their nature, would render the patient unconscious, rob him of the ability to pray, deprive him of the last merits which he could still acquire, and perhaps expose him to the danger of eternal perdition." [2]

[2] *"De Medicorum Obligationibus quoad Animas Aegrotantium";* Decrees of the Council of Quebec, XII.

This serious question of narcotics and anesthetics is treated in another chapter of this work,[3] and we refer the reader to it.

Another even more important question is that of the administration of the *Last Sacraments,* more especially of *Extreme Unction.* Every sick person in danger of death can and should receive Extreme Unction. Where does the danger of death commence and where does it end? This question has been much discussed, it has been wilfully complicated, and it has been said that it would be difficult to administer the Sacraments to all the sick merely because of the fear of having them die "unshriven, unhoused, unanealed." There are, as everyone knows, benign and mild diseases, and there are serious diseases; but the former can suddenly or gradually become serious, nay, even fatal. Hence the disease which gives warning of danger and demands the administration of Extreme Unction can only be a serious one. Extreme Unction, rightly understood, is not the Sacrament of the dying; it is more correctly called the *Scarament of the sick.* For this marvelous Sacrament, as the Church teaches us, was instituted for the spiritual and corporal relief of the sick. Beyond doubt, its most important task is to absolve the sick from their sins, to fortify them against temptations, and to facilitate a holy death. But it is impossible to

[3] *Supra,* Part III, Chap. VII, pp. 191 sqq.

mistake its secondary purpose, which is to give relief to the body and sometimes bring about its cure.
If there are some who doubt its profound influence
on physical life, priests and physicians, the happy
witnesses of divine grace, are there to testify to the
great power of this Sacrament in desperate cases.
We on our part have frequently had occasion to observe unexpected improvements and even cures
which left no doubt as to the efficacy of Extreme
Unction.

Msgr. Cortet, late bishop of Troyes, whom disease
had brought to the very portals of death and whom
Extreme Unction brought back to life, says: "Many
have a sort of horror of Extreme Unction; they
imagine that this Sacrament is not the Sacrament
of the sick, but of the dying, and that those who
have received it are inevitably doomed to die. This
is a fateful error, a prejudice based on ignorance of
the teachings of the Church; and if you have no
proof of that teaching, let me tell you that *I received
the last Sacraments several months ago, and not only
am I not dead, but they powerfully contributed to
bring me back to life."* [4]

The same bishop adds: "Since Our Lord Jesus
Christ, in His infinite mercy, has instituted a Sacrament so efficacious for the relief of the sick, and

---

[4] *Pastoral Letter to the faithful of the Diocese of Troyes,*
Feb. 1891.

its effects are so admirable and so certain, why is this Sacrament not zealously requested at the beginning of a serious illness? Why do the relatives in their blind and cruel affection, instead of calling the priest, keep him away until the patient asks for him? Sometimes someone dares to speak to a patient of Communion, but Extreme Unction is frequently postponed to the moment when, having lost all consciousness, he is no longer able to join in the motherly and fortifying prayers of the Church and to coöperate by his personal disposition with the efficaciousness of the Sacrament. Why is this? You hasten to call a physician as soon as disease appears among you, but you do not call upon the Supreme Physician of body and soul, who holds in His hands the keys of life and death! You carefully apply to your ills the remedies prescribed, you make the patient take even the bitterest draughts, you beg him to submit to the most painful operations; but you do not procure for him the spiritual medicine of Extreme Unction, which would vivify his body and soul!" It is impossible to place the true notion of this Sacrament in a better light or to portray more clearly the absurd and dangerous prejudices entertained by some people. Frequently the priest is not called until the dying man is insensible and perhaps unconscious. Is not this depriving the unfortunate patient of a precious help, and exposing the priest to making a useless trip to a corpse? Is it not, above all, depriving a beloved being of the merits of a free and conscious act and diminishing the fruits which he would have obtained from this Sacrament? Does the exhausted, insensible dying man, whom the minister of God addresses, know the significance of the unctions, does he understand the sacred words and the prayers which he should make? This is a secret known only to God; but, in doubt, it is evident that we ought, as much as possible, to assure the administration of the Sacrament to the sick before they are actually *in extremis*. The doctrine of the Church in this matter is stated as follows by the bishops of Canada, convened in council at Quebec: "Catholic physicians, though they are directly called by their profession to preserve physical life, must also consider that they have a serious duty of charity to fulfill in regard to the eternal salvation of the patients, which is far more important than the health of the body. They must, therefore, *either themselves or through others,* diligently and in time call the attention of the patient to the fact that he is in danger of death, and must be careful lest, allowing themselves to be guided by a culpable fear, they postpone this admonition until a time when the patient is prevented either by death or by the progress of his disease, or by the burden of his sufferings at the approaching end, from receiving the Sacraments with as much fruit as possible." [5]

The physician holds a position of trust and honor toward his patients; he alone can appreciate the nature of their disease, its probable or certain danger, and consequently it is his duty to warn them or their relatives. It is his imperative duty to advise that every patient in danger of death receive the Sacraments; and the decrees of the Church [6] have, at various times, called this duty to his attention, sometimes in rather severe terms. But though it is easy to accept and understand them in theory, it is difficult and sometimes impossible to follow them in practice; and every physician worthy of the name knows that this serious question of the Sacraments suggests or has suggested to him hard and complicated cases of conscience. Many authors have carefully studied these cases; they have attempted to specify their nature and to define the demands of justice and charity; but they could not attain their very laudable purpose, but only arrived at the vague conclusion that the obligations of duty vary with circumstances of time, place, and persons. The fact is that the duty of the physician toward the souls of his clients is superior to all mere calculations and

[5] See the decree quoted above.
[6] Decrees of Innocent III and Pius V.

cannot be reduced to any definite formula. Let us, therefore, be satisfied with indicating the rule which should guide the practitioner who is anxious both to perform the duties of his noble profession and to obey the laws of the Church.

The physician must be honest and sincere, keep the family informed of his fears, and not conceal from the patient the seriousness of his disease. Conscious of his mission, anxious to discharge his responsibility, he must not deceive him who has placed all his confidence in him, and nourish vain illusions by lying promises, thus making himself an accomplice of those false friends who try to deceive the patient as to his true condition and to take from him every idea of danger, under the pretext of not frightening him and of sparing him the terrors of death. It goes without saying that duty does not exclude reason, and that prudence goes hand in hand with courage. Caution is always necessary, as conscience also dictates, in dealing with a man who is weakened by disease, exhausted by suffering, and whose will is no longer strong enough to resist vivid impressions. We should not say to such a man, "You are lost, you have but a few hours to live," nor promise him a rapid and certain recovery; but to his anxious questions we should respond in commonplace and general phrases: "Yes, you are very sick; your case is serious; recovery will take a long time," and we should also add some few words of hope, if hope there be to mitigate what seems the severe verdict of science: "Worse cases have been cured; have patience; the cure depends on God and time; I can promise you nothing, but everything possible will be done," etc.

This is the only rule applicable to the generality of patients, especially to those who have no religion, but are indifferent or hostile. In the case of those who are Christians, a greater frankness is of obligation; and we should not fear to make them listen to the admonition of death and to urge them to receive the Sacraments without delay.

The doctor should never lose his solicitude for the soul of the patient, but promptly inform the family when the danger of death arises. His intervention will be more or less governed by circumstances. Sometimes he must limit himself to the words, "The case is serious, nay desperate; if you have any affairs, spiritual or temporal, to put in order, it is time to think of them." If the relatives refuse to fulfill this duty of charity, or delay in discharging it, the physician must discreetly choose the most expeditious and effective means of assuring to his patient the succor of religion. He may inform the priest, or the Sisters or Brothers of the parish, or it may be some friend or neighbor of the family, and see to it that the dying person is properly prepared for death. If none of these means are possible or practicable, he himself is bound only to inform the patient in as far as he believes that his intervention will be successful and efficacious.

In administering the Sacraments to the dying, especially in contagious, eruptive cases, the priest must, before every anointing, carefully wipe any metal rod he may use, and, in case of necessity, pass it through a flame of fire, before plunging it anew into the oilstocks.[7] Without this precaution the Holy Oils might become a source of infection.

In the case of dying infants the first question to be asked is whether they are baptized. In our epoch of religious indifference we know what negligence parents frequently manifest in assuring to their children the benefits of the Sacrament of regeneration; many children are not baptized for six months, a year, two years, or more. In such cases the duty of the physician is to urge the necessity of Baptism and, when necessary, to administer Baptism himself.

Older children, whether they have made their first Communion or not, have, as far as the physician is concerned, a right to the same solicitude as an adult; they have a right, when in danger of death, to the

[7] If the priest uses cotton, he should use a fresh piece at each anointing and burn the used one for the reasons given above. He should not use his thumb in contagious, eruptive diseases, because he may contract the disease himself and also infect the holy oils. (Translator.)

same spiritual succor as adults, and, since the ignorance of parents on this point is often extreme, it may be well to remove it by informing them that the ministry of the priest is always useful at this age, and that it can do a great deal of good, but never any harm.

# CHAPTER V

## CONSCIOUSNESS OF THE DYING

THE sick, in their last agony, have a more or less clear understanding of the seriousness of their condition, but they do not always feel the approach of the last hour. Sometimes the brain is affected by disease and they are plunged into a coma, which robs them of all consciousness; sometimes the intellect, affected through the brain by the decay of the organism, is so weakened that it loses the just comprehension of things. But it should be remembered that in many cases the condition of the soul does not correspond to the condition of the body. In most desperate conditions the soul has been known to guard its self-possession and serenity even after horrible injuries, and that in spite of the involvement of essential organs or of total disorganization. Whether or not we can explain this astonishing contradiction, it is a fact that the dying frequently preserve a remarkable self-control and fortitude, and that God gives to many the grace of conversion at the last moment, when, as by a flash, they perceive their true condition and obtain pardon for their sins by an act of perfect contrition.

Observation has demonstrated the unexpected return, at the hour of death, of the highest faculties of the soul, which disease had subjugated and which were believed forever lost. Beethoven, when he was about to surrender his soul to his Maker, recovered his speech and his hearing, which faculties he had apparently lost, and which he made use of to communicate to those about him some of those sublime chords which have been called his "Prayer to God." Learned savants on their deathbed have had intuitions which furnished the solution of problems long sought for in vain; dying poets have received from the Muses their best inspiration, and philosophers have been favored with new and profound concepts. And if we would wish to speak of simple Christians, who have generously given themselves to God, and whom God has, in return, richly endowed with graces and illuminations, and of those whom the Church has ranked among her invisible protectors, what surprising deaths, what sweet and superb last moments, what calmness of spirit, in spite of terrible afflictions of the flesh, and what clear-sightedness and grandeur of thought have not many of them shown in the hour of death!

Nay, even more, reason has sometimes been restored to those who had seemingly lost it; in other

words, the insane have been cured of their affliction at the moment when they were about to leave
this world. This return of an intelligent and free
soul, in spite of physical decrepitude brought about
by incurable disease, is an extremely startling phen-
omenon, of which many authors have made mention, but which still remains unexplained. Brierre de
Boismont, a celebrated French alienist, reported a
number of such cases observed by himself; in one of
these cases the use of reason was recovered after two
years of alienation.[1] Priests, and especially the chap-
lains of asylums, must always bear this eventuality
in mind in the case of dying lunatics.

Children who are about to die, especially as a result of organic disease or debility, have sometimes
uttered thoughts and reflections far "beyond their
years," and have manifested a degree of intelligence
and a reasoning power almost mature. People are
astonished at this precocity which suddenly reveals
itself at the portals of death. They say that such
children "are too intelligent to live" or that they
"are ripe for Heaven"; but no one is able to explain
the development of the spirit in an exhausted and
dying organism. This observation is not rare, but it
is of extreme importance in regard to the administration of the Sacraments. Even very young children can understand the meaning of the Sacraments

[1] *Annales Médico-Psychologiques,* Vol. II, p. 531.

and obtain their fruits. Some well instructed children have been known to demand the Sacraments with great persistence and to have received them with manifestations of a truly angelic piety. It is the business of the priest to judge of the interior dispositions and the spiritual state of little children as well as of the spiritual succor which they need.

All these facts and many others which we cannot here enumerate, clearly demonstrate that the intelligence does not depend absolutely either on the health of the body or the integrity of the brain. It is impossible to explain these phenomena, and they are in contradiction with certain scientific theories, but they command the assent of every impartial observer, and what evidence is superior to observation in such cases?

The practical consequences which flow from these observations are extremely important. We must not judge of the intellectual caliber of a man from his appearance and the condition of his health, nor of the mental state of a dying man from his insensibility or torpor. There is always danger of identifying the state of the brain with the condition of the soul. It is never too late to call the priest and to administer the Sacraments. As long as there is life, the Sacraments of Penance and Extreme Unction exercise their efficacy, and the patient can obtain from them abundant fruits of salvation, even if he

is apparently lifeless and gives no sign of consciousness. Therefore, it is a grave duty, even in desperate
cases, to have recourse to the ministry of a priest,
which is never useless, sometimes produces unexpected results, and always gives hope and consolation
to the sorrowing relatives.

How many times is not the priest, and also the
physician, called to a dying man who has been suddenly prostrated or whom the progress of disease
has unexpectedly deprived of consciousness! The
immobility of the patient gives him the appearance
of a corpse. The relatives doubt the efficaciousness
of any aid and call both priest and doctor to satisfy
custom, or in order "not to have anything with
which to reproach themselves." Is there nothing to
be done in such a case? The eye is weakened and insensible, sight is lost, there is no sign of sensibility;
and yet in the midst of this decay the faculty of hearing frequently remains more or less intact.[2] Speak

[2] It is not only in cases of sudden death that hearing remains almost to the last. I was witness to an instance verifying
this statement. An old man, a nonagenarian, had to all appearance died of a lingering cancer of the throat. I was present
and said the prayers for the dying. He was pronounced dead.
His heart-beats could no longer be felt. No doctor was present
with a stethoscope. I finished the prayers.

Ten to fifteen minutes had elapsed since he was declared
dead. I arose, and before I could leave the room an ungrate-
ful and profligate son started a quarrel about the division of
the property. I was about to speak to him of the impropriety

to the patient, who no longer seems to belong to this world, in various tones of voice and repeatedly, and it may happen that he will hear and understand you; he may even answer your questions by a movement of the head or, more often, by a slight pressure of the hand. Confession *in extremis* has been heard in this manner, and this fact must always be kept in mind. As to the physician, he also has his part to play in such cases; we have already mentioned the resources which medical science puts at his disposal to stimulate the dying and to facilitate the ministrations of the priest.

It is said that an archbishop who was seriously ill and felt the end coming sent to his neighboring confrère to come without delay and give him Extreme Unction. When the bishop arrived, the dying prelate was in a coma and gave no sign of consciousness. While the preparations for administering Extreme Unction were made, the assistants lamented the unconscious condition of the patient which would not permit him to unite himself to the prayers of the Church and to coöperate with the operation of grace. But, O wonder! during the ceremony the

of his actions, when lo and behold! the supposedly dead man, who had lain dying from four o'clock the day before until ten the next day, sat up in bed, opened his glassy eyes, looked toward his son, and tried to point at him, whilst his lips moved as if he wished to speak; then he suddenly dropped back to rise no more. (Translator.)

hands of the dying archbishop which had lain with the palms up on the coverlet, slowly turned round [3] at the moment the ministering bishop was ready to anoint them. This was a certain and touching proof that the pious archbishop, who to all appearances was unconscious, was aware of the fact that he was being anointed.

[3] Laymen are anointed on the palm of the hand, priests on the back of the hand.

# CHAPTER VI

### THE MOMENT OF DEATH

THE question at what precise moment death occurs, is directly connected with the important question of Extreme Unction. It has been the subject of numerous works.

The double and imperative necessity of not exposing a dying person to the danger of being deprived of this Sacrament, and of not profaning the Sacrament by administering it to one who is already dead, gives rise to the difficult problem: "What is the exact moment of death? When does the soul depart from the body?"

It was long thought that after the heart had ceased to beat, the subject was dead. It has, however, been shown that the injection of adrenalin may again start heart-beats that had ceased for some time. This shows that apparent death may precede real death by at least that interval.

In a case of "apparent death," if there is room for the least doubt, it is the duty of the physician to use the greatest reserve in drawing his conclusions and to advise the priest to exercise his ministry conditionally. Simple prudence demands that nothing be neglected to assure the benefit of the last Sacraments to the dying, even when they appear to be dead, and not to deprive them of any chance, be it ever so small, of saving their souls.

If no physician is present, those about the dying person have certain special obligations. Since they are ignorant of the resources of medicine, and incapable of distinguishing apparent death from real death, their first duty is to let no opportunity of being useful to the dying person escape them, and especially to procure for him spiritual succor, even *sub conditione*,[1] without delay.

The question, considered in the abstract, as to the moment at which the body ceases to live, is one which would take us too deeply into the most difficult points of biology. As we see it, the body is not dead as long as any part of it, any group of cells, is alive. Practically, in a given case, no man can tell when the last cell in an apparently dead body has ceased to live. It cannot however be more than a few hours.

---

[1] The priest will absolve an unconscious person conditionally, whilst he can anoint him with the sole condition, *"if thou art still alive."* Hence, we repeat, it is never too late to call the priest as long as there is the least possibility of latent life still existing.

# CHAPTER VII

## CARE OF THE DEAD

IF the dying have a right to our solicitude, the dead demand our respect. True, a corpse is but an inert mass about to be delivered to the worms and to destruction; but it is also the former domicile of an immortal soul, with which it was intimately united during life and whose faults as well as merits it shared, and with which it will be reunited on the Day of Judgment.

In order to comply with the conventions, as well as to give death time to accomplish its work, the corpse should be touched and moved about as little as possible before the appearance of rigidity. The custom of undressing the corpse immediately after death in order to hastily give it a bath, etc., cannot be sufficiently condemned.

The ancient custom of pulling the bed-sheet over the face of the deceased is dangerous and unbecoming. On the contrary, *to close the eyes* of the deceased, when they remain open or half-open, is a pious and laudable office usually confided to a close relative or very dear friend.

285

The lower jaw, as we have said, often hangs down and the mouth remains open after the last breath. It is customary to close it by tying up the chin with a handkerchief, folded like a bandage and tightly knotted on top of the head. This precaution is excellent and should be taken in time, *i. e.,* before muscular rigidity sets in, yet not precipitately, before death is certain. In this regard the physician frequently has occasion to temper the indecent haste of relatives, especially in the case of old people.

As soon as the fact of death is established, the body should be laid on its back, with the arms extended downward or crossed on the breast, but not tied. These precautions are taken in order not to hinder motion if life remains, which is always possible, no matter how improbable, and to await cadaveric rigidity.

Some hygienic precautions may be added. The death chamber should be well aired. Sheets are to be laid under the corpse to protect the mattress and floor against evacuations. An antiseptic deodorant, such as calcium chloride, is never harmful, and may do great service. A certain quantity should be placed in saucers for evaporation.

The corpse should never be left alone. The *death-watch,* which is deeply rooted in our customs, has its *raison d'être.* Besides complying with the laudable desire of honoring the deceased and praying for the repose of his soul, it offers an occasion of providing for the problematical hazards of apparent death.

The corpse quickly decomposes and therefore must soon be consigned to the earth if not embalmed. In the case of contagious diseases, and especially during epidemics, the authorities may require early burial.

# CHAPTER VIII

Is capital punishment authorized by the moral law
of nature, or does it exceed the limits of social justice? Is capital punishment absolutely necessary to
safeguard society from crime? These are grave and
difficult questions, which philanthropists of all ages
have raised, but not solved. They do not belong to
our competency and it is not our intention to
discuss them. We accept the traditional opinion that
the penalty inflicted on convicted criminals constitutes for them both a punishment and an expiation,
and at the same time rids society temporarily or
forever of a dangerous member and gives a salutary
example to all. But there are two conditions required in order that the punishment of human justice, which is but a reflection of Eternal Justice, may
be just. It must be proportioned to the fault and it
must be neither excessive nor barbarous, always
constituting a punishment and not a vengeance.

Capital punishment is justly inflicted upon those

who have voluntarily killed a fellow-man,[1] and we shall here simply examine the various modes of capital punishment from the standpoint of morality. That a dangerous criminal must be suppressed is generally admitted; but our conception of the demands of justice is that, in removing him from society, he should not be made to die slowly amid horrible tortures, and that man should not usurp the rights of God as the avenger of sin.[2]

Putting murderers to death by torture (beating, scourging, the rack, etc.) is no longer in vogue; this method has been abolished for quite some time under the pressure of public opinion, and cowardly and useless cruelties are indignantly condemned by all right-thinking people.

*Death by fire* is no less horrible and blameable. This was the torture which thousands of the early Christians suffered during the persecutions and which was inflicted upon the angelic and valiant Joan of Arc, that noble martyr who has recently been canonized by the Church.

What shall we say of those other frightful methods of executing criminals which the revolutionary upheaval of the 18th century caused to disappear? Christian nations long tolerated these abuses, not

---

[1] *"Omnes qui acceperint gladium gladio peribunt."* (Matth. XXVI, 52.)

[2] *"Revenge is mine, saith the Lord."*

only without protest, but with a sort of fierce pleasure, and our great-grandparents witnessed them without a shudder. They were the following: the breaking of the bones and placing the broken body on a moving wheel (*the wheel*); dragging the person to death by tying him to a horse's tail; tearing the body to pieces by tying the four limbs to four strong horses, which pulled in different directions (*quartering*); dislocation of the arms by raising the body high and suddenly dropping it, after having tied the hands behind the back (*estrapade* or *strapado*); forcing a long pointed pole implanted in the ground through the body (*impalement*); the slow killing by throwing stones upon the condemned man (*stoning*); etc. Thanks be to God, these punishments no longer exist.[3] There is no proportion between them and the crime committed, no matter what it may be, for which they used to be inflicted. There are less barbarous means of executing criminals, among them *drowning*, which has been in use from time immemorial. But it must be confessed that, though death by drowning is sure, it is very slow and frequently accompanied by terrible suffering. Hence

[3] In America, mob violence sometimes inflicts similar barbarous punishments, and all too frequently such violence is tolerated and condoned. The very ones who oppose capital punishment by the State recur to the barbarous punishments of former ages (Translator.)

*drowning* cannot be recommended as a humane method of capital punishment.

Asphyxia by *strangulation* is very much in vogue even to-day. There are two methods : the condemned man is either hanged by means of a rope or placed against a stake and a rope tied about his neck. The rope is then twisted by means of a stick (*garrotting*). In both cases asphyxia is not rapid and is accompanied by convulsive movements of the members, which betray great suffering; the grimaces of the face are so terrible that the head of the condemned man is often covered with a black hood. Hanging is a crude and barbarous method of execution, which we cannot approve.[4]

Under certain conditions recourse is had to shooting (*firing squad*). If done by skilled marksmen, shooting is a very expeditious method; but if it is entrusted to unskilled hands, it exposes the condemned person to unnecessary suffering.[5] The vic-

[4] Can the question of sensible suffering be brought in where the trap is sprung and the neck broken? We think not, since the breaking of the neck renders the culprit unconscious. (Translator.)

[5] In the beginning of September, 1908, the European newspapers reported a remarkable case of death by shooting, which, however, proves that this method of execution, even though performed by skilful men, may involve real cruelty. A revolutionist was arrested during the disorders in Russia and condemned to death. A detachment of twelve soldiers was detailed

tims of the Commune of 1871, among them such holy martyrs as Darboy, Deguerry, Olivaint, Ducoudray, and Captier, suffered much from the unskilled rudeness of their executioners.

*Decapitation,* or beheading, which has always been widely in use, consists in cutting off the head at the neck with a sword or ax. It is a manner of execution the efficacy of which varies according to the sureness of the executioner; sometimes death is instantaneous, whereas at other times it is prolonged and cruel. Thanks to the initiative of two physicians, Louis and Guillotin, the *guillotine* provided a sure and swift means of execution at the end of the 18th century.[6]

to execute him. Twelve bullets actually hit him, but not a single wound was mortal. The man fell and was left lying as a warning to others. After some time, however, he recovered and crawled to a near-by farmer's cottage, where he received loving care, and after a few weeks was able to return to the scene of his former activity. The police, however, recognized him and arrested him again, and this time he was condemned to two years in the penitentiary on account of other crimes attributed to him. (Dr. Sleumer.)

[6] A few years ago, Hector Fleischmann, in his book, *Die Guillotine im Jahre 1793,* proved that neither Dr. Antony Louis, then surgeon at the Salpêtrière in Paris, nor Dr. Guillotin ( + March 26, 1814) had anything to do with the invention of the guillotine. It was invented by a German piano-maker named Tobias Schmidt, then living in Paris, and was sold to the government for 824 francs. Many similarly constructed gibbets were soon built in other cities. (Dr. Sleumer.)

In recent years electricity has been employed as a means of capital punishment (*electrocution*). Since its puissant action has been demonstrated by the instantaneously fatal shocks received by individuals who inadvertently touched high-voltage wires, it was believed that it would put an end to human existence much more quickly than any other means and that it would spare the condemned man all suffering. The United States were the first to introduce the "electric chair," and the first electrocution took place in 1890. This execution, as is well known, was a failure, and we shall not recall the sad and barbarous details recounted in the newspapers of the time. In spite of the use of a strong current, the condemned man was not immediately killed, but suffered a long and horrible agony. His death was not really certain until the body had been literally cremated. Since then the "electric chair" has been improved and now functions successfully.[7]

At one time *poison* was administered to criminals; its effects necessarily varied according to the subject's power of resistance, and the nature and dose of the poison administered. This method of executing criminals gives a bad example to the public and does not comply with the conditions required to make the punishment an act of public expiation.

[7] Much has been learned of late years concerning the action of electricity. (Translator.)

Condemned criminals have sometimes been made to take a dose of strong poison on condition that they would be pardoned if they escaped death. Such a penalty, depending on the criminal's vital resistance and the purity of the drugs administered, is rather haphazard and therefore to be condemned. It is no longer in use.

Another practice, which ancient opinion accepted, and which was in use as late as the 16th century, appears to us no less worthy of condemnation. The victim was handed over to scientists with full permission to subject him to dangerous experiments for the benefit of humanity. We believe that physiological and medical experimenting on human beings should be confined to narrow limits and that beyond these limits they become barbarous and immoral for the reasons set forth in the ninth and tenth chapters of Part III, *supra.*

Shall we speak of another method of execution, once very common? The victim was tied or nailed by the hands to two pieces of wood, which crossed each other. The body hung bleeding and broken between heaven and earth until death ensued, Alas! This was the martyrdom inflicted upon our Divine Master, Jesus Christ, the Son of God! Can we express or feel all its odium when we know that it was the fault of our culpable hearts? This instrument of unspeakable torture, reserved for the lowest

criminals, was precisely the one chosen by the Divine
Mediator on which to suffer for us and to satisfy
Divine Justice. Since Constantine the Great cruci-
fixion has been no longer inflicted upon criminals
(at least in civilized lands), and the "tree of death"
remains the adorable sign of the Innocent Victim.
Let us not forget that it is also the tree of our salvation, and our lips will never find for it any other words
than those of love and adoration. *"O Crux, ave!"*

# CHAPTER IX

By cremation we mean the method of disposing of a corpse by incinerating it instead of burying it in the ground according to ancient custom. Its promoters claim that cremation has such great advantages over all other known modes that it is destined to replace them in the near future. In matter of fact, however, it is not practical, constitutes a danger to public morality, and is employed as a machine of war against the Catholic Church.

In the beginning cremation found Christian believers indifferent, but not hostile. The arguments from hygiene with which it bolstered its cause, silenced all suspicion. It pretended to respect all creeds and, according to the statements of its defenders, had nothing whatever to do with religion. The Church at first neither approved nor condemned the practice, but simply ignored it. Some writers asserted that cremation was permitted, while others claimed it was merely tolerated.

There was good reason for this initial silence;

but to-day the Church definitely condemns cremation.
She has laid down the following rules: [1]

1. The clergy must refuse public prayers and access to
the church to the bodies of those who, while alive,
ordered their bodies to be cremated.

2. A Catholic may not demand cremation either for
his own body or that of others.

3. Catholics are forbidden to belong to societies
whose object is to promote cremation.

We could close this chapter here, but deem it more
worthy of ourselves and of our faith to prove that
the attitude of the Church is based upon reason, and
that even before the Holy See acted, science had condemned cremation.

One of the advantages of cremation is supposed
to be the diminution or suppression of the danger
of contagion from transmissible or epidemic diseases.
But in matter of fact cremation multiplies the causes
of infection. Its preliminaries are longer and more
dangerous than those of burial; they consist of:
(1) a complete autopsy; (2) placing the body in the
coffin; (3) transporting it to the crematory; (4) taking it from the coffin; [2] (5) placing it in the furnace.

[1] Response of the Holy Office, May 19, 1886.
[2] Some American crematories now incinerate body and coffin together. In that case this objection falls. *Cycl. Americana*,
"Cremation of the Dead." See also *Catholic Encyclopedia*,
"Cremation." Here may be added, as Dr. Sleumer has done in

This process of incineration lasts from an hour to an hour and a half. It is tedious and expensive, and causes an abundant liberation of noxious gasses, which, however, thanks to an ingenious contrivance, are not discharged directly into the outer air, but are intercepted an destroyed by a coke-fire halfway up the chimney. In modern crematories the process is entirely hidden from view. It is, besides, usual to-day for the mourners to depart as soon as the body is placed in the incinerator.

The cremation of a corpse must, as we have said, be in each instance preceded by a complete autopsy, to obviate the greatest objection against it, which is that it makes judicial exhumation impossible. We know how important judicial exhumations can be. Sometimes they convict the guilty and then again they save the innocent. It is decidedly in the interest of society to preserve this benefit. With the incineration of bodies, which destroys toxic salts and causes other poisons (arsenic, phosphorus) to disappear, legal medicine would lose its meaning, and fail to reveal traces of crime. The from four to six pounds of white mineral residue which remains after the cremation of a corpse would not only be of no use

his German translation, that Dr. Surbled had in mind zinc-lined or metal coffins used in transportation. Not every village or even small city can have its own crematory.—*Tr.*

to justice, but might even lead it astray; for it would be as easy to change or disperse the ashes as it is difficult to rob a grave, open a coffin, or abuse a corpse. Hence moral teaching and science agree in condemning cremation.

The world is horrified, especially in times of epidemic, when death knows no rest and in a few hours destroys many lives. The advocates of cremation have taken this popular sentiment into account and skilfully exploited it; they have pretended that the deleterious germs and bacteria, the cause of epidemics, are fostered and propagated by cemeteries, and that cremation alone has the power of destroying them.

In the following chapter we shall deal with the important subject of cemeteries. Precise rules must govern the organization and upkeep of cemeteries, and neglect of these rules constitutes a real danger to public health. The discussions aroused have at least this advantage that they will call the attention of scientists to the matter.

With this reservation we may say that burial (inhumation) corresponds to the laws of hygiene as well as to the demands of moral teaching, whereas cremation, which some would like to substitute for it, serves the interests of free thought, and not those of humanity.

# CHAPTER X

SINCE every corpse is subject to complete decomposition, pains have always been taken to remove dead bodies from sight and, as far as possible, to prevent the atmosphere of the living from being polluted by the numerous products of decomposition.

*Cemeteries* are plots of ground set apart to receive the bodies of the deceased. The bodies taken there for burial are previously enveloped in a shroud [1] and placed in a tightly closed coffin. All the rules governing funerals are dictated both by respect for the dead and by the demands of hygiene for the preservation of public health.

The corpse, after having been bathed, is wrapped in a piece of linen (*shroud* or *winding sheet*) and deposited in a casket made of wood or metal. These coverings protect the corpse and insure its isolation. [2] Sometimes a lead coffin is placed around the wooden

[1] In America the shroud is no longer in use. A coffin and an outer box are customary.—(Tr.)

[2] In this country the body is clothed as usual and placed in a coffin, made of various materials, according to the price. It is also lined with cloth or silk, according to price, making it a real bed of rest.—(Tr.)

one and hermetically sealed. In many instances the interior of the coffin is lined with metal to make it waterproof.

In spite of all these precautions decomposition runs its course, though slowly, as a rule. When it is advisable to hasten the process artificially, means to this end may be freely employed.[3]

*Embalming,* which is performed by injecting an antiseptic and astringent fluid into the blood vessels, is the best method of avoiding putrefaction and is coming more widely into use from year to year.[4]

The place of sepulture has varied with the ages,

[3] In America, where almost all bodies are embalmed, these procedures would be superfluous.—Tr.

[4] The method now commonly employed in the United States is an injection of the fluid into the common iliac artery, a counter opening for the escape of blood being made in the corresponding vein. In women the axillary artery and vein are often employed. The abdominal cavity and the intestines are also injected. The fluid consists chiefly of formalin, with, perhaps, mercuric chloride, zinc chloride, and other chemicals. Bodies so prepared can be preserved for months at ordinary temperatures. Embalming has taken the place of ice in preserving the dead until the funeral services. The reasons for this are its preservation of the body for transportation and leisurely disposal and its absolute prevention of communication of infection, either before the body is buried or after it has crumbled and mingled with earth in a cemetery. *Cycl. Americana, s. v.* "Embalming." Since this method of embalming destroys any spark of life in a person, embalmers must make sure that the person is dead, before entering upon their task. This is especially the case with neurotics, who may easily be in a state of hysterical lethargy. Dr. Thoinot says: "The

according to the respect entertained for the dead, and especially according to the cultural conditions of various peoples. In former times, and even to-day in country parishes, the burial-places surround the church, and more than one corpse is buried in each grave.[5] The health of the people living round about has never suffered any damage from the proximity of the cemetery, while their piety found a source of sweet and precious consolation therein. It must, however, be admitted that the smallness of cemeteries and the burial of many bodies in the same grave is sometimes in flagrant conflict with the laws of hygiene, and ignorance grafted on ancient custom did not try to find a remedy. Furthermore the mortuary vaults in the cellars of churches were frequently narrow and damp and apt to become harmful to the health of the living. With the increase of population and the growing demands of urban life and

duration of the *attack of sleep* (this expression is synonymous with hysteric lethargy) is quite variable; while at times very brief, a half-hour, for example, it may extend over entire days, months, and sometimes, it is said, even years. It is then a case of *apparent death,* and note well that as matter of fact *all the celebrated cases of apparent death and marvellous resurrection* arise from hysteric lethargy." Thoinot-Weysse, *Medico-Legal Moral Offences,* p. 150). Therefore, the cautions recommended in Chapters III and VII should still be observed, especially when the subject has not yet been declared dead by a physician.

[5] In country parishes in America the cemetery is usually near, though not immediately surrounding the church.

public health, the cemeteries have been removed from the sacred precincts of the parish church and located at some distance from the cities. Their site and arrangement should comply with many conditions, which, we are sorry to say, in spite of existing regulations, are not always fulfilled as carefully as they should.

Cemeteries should be at least 350 meters [6] distant from city or town. No house should be build within 300 feet of a burial-ground. These measures, hardly sufficient for cities, are frequently not observed.[7] The regulations concerning depth and length of graves and their distance apart are but seldom observed. The burial of a number of bodies in the same grave should be avoided.

The ground destined for the burial of bodies should be hard clay, if possible on an elevated spot, far from rivers or wells. It should be planted with trees such as willows or poplars, which by their long roots absorb the putrid liquids and thus help to keep the soil dry. If, in spite of all precautions, the water penetrates the soil, good drainage should be provided.

The simultaneous burial of many in a common grave, so severely condemned by science, prohibited by law in many places, sometimes becomes a real

[6] About a quarter of a mile.
[7] See *Catholic Encyc., s. v.* "Cremation."

necessity in large cities. The incidental danger can to some extent be averted by covering the coffins with unslaked lime and stopping further burials as soon as the grave is filled.

Generally speaking, cemeteries, with some easily realized reforms, will insure the absolute disintegration of corpses under the conditions demanded by hygiene; and we need not be intimidated by the criticisms of the partisans of cremation.[8]

The sense of smell is not offended in cemeteries because the exhalations do not come to the surface, but the gases combine with the mineral matter in the soil or are retained by absorption.[9] Even in vaults the presence of gases is problematical. Tardieu holds that they are rare. Finally, what are these dreaded gases except those which we constantly encounter (carbon dioxide, ammonia, etc.) which are not toxic in the diluted state in which they are usually found?[10]

The alleged infiltration of the subsoil and the pollution of rivers by cemeteries has never been

[8] *Questions d'Hygiène Sociale,* 1891, p. 304.

[9] See *Catholic Encyc., s. v.* "Cremation."

[10] If we wanted to keep these gases out of the air, we should have to forbid many things which generate them, and which are not strictly necessary, *e. g.,* the driving of automobiles for pleasure. The auto traffic on any state or federal highway causes a greater infusion into the air of a much deadlier gas (carbon monoxide), in one day than do a hundred cemeteries in a hundred years. (Translator.)

proven. The water of wells located in cemeteries has been analyzed, and no more organic matter was found in them than in other wells. Of course, this water need not be used for drinking. Finally, it is by no means an established fact that a cemetery, after having received the bodies of persons who died of an infectious disease, contributes to the propagation of the disease. "A case still remains to be cited," Dr. Rochard remarks, "of an epidemic which originated in a cemetery."

It is to be regretted that young fetuses are not always buried in a cemetery. This should be made obligatory for all fetuses over six weeks old. The present practice is opposed both to hygiene and to moral 'teaching, and permits the performance and concealment of criminal abortions. Undeveloped embryos are interred in yards and gardens, cast into rivers and toilets, and sometimes even into the garbage can or fed to dogs.

Maritime life has its own special mode of burial, imposed by necessity. The dead are thrown into the sea.[11] Where inhumation is possible, it retains all its advantages, and we cannot but deplore the barbarous and unhygienic custom of the Hindoos who throw their dead into the Ganges, where they quickly rot and become the prey of vultures and crocodiles.

[11] This is a rule now practiced only on ships which are at sea for a long voyage.

# INDEX

307